Whidbey Landmarks

Stories and Poems
from Whidbey Island

BOOKS BY WHIDBEY WRITERS' GROUP

Beneath the Rain Shadow (1994)

Beneath the Rain Shadow II (1996)

Beneath the Rain Shadow III (1999)

Take Our Words for Whidbey (2002)

Whispers in the Mist (2004)

Whidbey Connections (2007)

Whidbey Writes Again (2010)

Write Around Whidbey (2015)

Whidbey Landmarks

Stories and Poems
From Whidbey Island

Whidbey Writers'
Group

Whidbey Writers' Group Press
Coupeville, WA

First Edition
Printed in the USA

We dedicate this book to

Susan Terhune Nunn
and
Gordon M. Labuhn

In Memoriam
Nasus Nunn and Gordon Labuhn

Nasus – Susan spelled backwards – lived up to the moniker: Poet Laureate of Whidbey Writers' Group. Besides writing poetry, Nasus often struggled to steer our group meetings away from idle chatter and back to the business of critiquing each other's writing – with varying degrees of success. After college she flew the then-friendly skies as an airline stewardess long before they morphed into flight attendants. Once retired on Whidbey Island, Nasus joined Beach Watchers and worked tirelessly to protect the beautiful, but fragile environment. Living but a short walk from a bluff overlooking the Strait of Juan de Fuca and her beloved Salish Sea, many of her poems reflected what she saw around her. We miss Nasus and her evocative words.

After joining WWG, somewhat like Nasus, Gordon tried to infuse us with more structure. He and his spreadsheets met with limited success and frequent eye rolls, but we valued his motives and efforts. We came to marvel at the depth and breadth of Gordon's life through the yarns he spun – always featuring his unique wit. Renaissance man seems way overused, but it certainly applied to Gordon. He grew up in inner-city Detroit as a "gang leader" – though his gang more closely resembled The Little Rascals. In various life phases, he produced films, wrote and presented management guides, sailed boats, skied, preached, and wrote damn-fine mysteries. We all miss him.

Table of Contents

x

Avis Rector

Whidbey Island has been home to Avis Rector all her life. She and her husband, both retired teachers, raised cattle on their Monroe Landing Farm for sixty-five years. Taking pictures of their grandson exploring the farm, led her to publish a picture book Carl Helps *on the Farm. Avis used her lifetime experiences and stories she heard from her family to create her novel,* Pauline, A New Beginning *on Whidbey Island. She is currently working on a sequel,* Pauline's Family, Their Life *on Whidbey Island. Avis enjoys sharing flowers and vegetables from her garden and walks on the island beaches.*

We Moved a Landmark

Clusters of daffodils with yellow blooms standing tall among the grass and weeds remind me of a time before bulldozers plowed their way over the fields, pushing soil and brush to level the ground where our house once stood.

It's a sunny day in March 2014 and a friend has brought my husband and me to this place of my childhood. We wander several hundred feet over the uneven ground, careful not to trip over chunks of concrete that once made up the foundations of our house and barns. We stop and look south at acres of runways and the Whidbey Island Naval Air Station buildings. Our friend says we can go no farther as we are trespassing and a patrol car might come this way.

We turn and walk to the beach. *My beach!* We step around the sticky sand verbena and clamber over sun-bleached logs. I stoop and bring handfuls of gray fine-grained sand close to my face, savoring the smell of salt and seaweed. Memories float in my head as the sand sifts through my fingers. Small wavelets wash over mounds of smooth pebbles. I look for agates, and then to the sky. The noise is deafening. A jet plane makes a touch-and-go landing. "Shall we go?" our friend asks. I glance back at Mom's daffodils, and then we follow him back to his Jeep.

Chris and Margareta Weidenbach, who were my grandparents, purchased the 267-acre beachfront

Ocean View Farm from Amelia Hoffman in 1915.
They worked hard clearing and farming the land with
their young family—my father, Henry, his brother,
Ed, and two sisters, Anna and Dora.

My dad won the heart of Genevra Kellogg, a
teacher at the Cornet School. They married in June
1920 and moved into a one-room house on the farm.
A few years later, his brother, Ed, married Eunice
Boyer, and they moved into another small house on
the farm.

In 1926, Chris and Margareta divided the farm
land between the two brothers, and with a growing
family, Henry decided it was time to build a larger
house.

After reading my mother's old letters, I can
imagine a scenario such as the following:

"Genevra, it's time we have a new house. This
one is just too small."

"Henry, are you sure we can afford it?"

"We'll borrow money from the folks. I talked
with Dad about it yesterday, but I'm not sure Mom
will go along with it."

Henry soon talked with his mother, the family
bookkeeper. She gave her permission with the
condition that Henry make monthly payments on the
loan and that it be paid in full in ten years. Papers
were signed and notarized.

Henry chose a spot on the bluff above the lagoon
that ran parallel to West Beach. Genevra sketched

preliminary plans for a two-story, four-bedroom house with a full basement. After living in the dark one-room house for many years, she designed all the rooms with many windows including beautiful leaded-glass panels across the top of two large picture windows in the living room.

A skilled carpenter earned about fifteen dollars a day in 1928, and Henry wanted a good one. He hired Otto Van Dyk, who in 1913 had built the Neil Barn, now known as The Roller Barn, to oversee the construction of the house.

In 1930, although the upstairs rooms had no walls, they settled into the house with their children—Howard, Marjorie and Eldon. Avis joined the family in 1933, and then Ray in 1935. Genevra loved her spacious kitchen. She and Henry welcomed family and friends. It was a happy home.

The government bought many farms in Clover Valley in 1941, but not the Weidenbach farms. The families had lived as good neighbors to NAS Whidbey Island at Ault Field for many years. In 1958, they and many of their neighbors were informed by the government that they would all have to vacate their farms because longer runways were needed for the new jets.

When we learned that our house could be bought back from the government for $600, the wheels in my head started spinning. After all, I considered the family home to be *my house* since I was the only one of five children to be born in it, and I sure didn't like the idea of bulldozers destroying it. The house had withstood west winds and rainstorms off Puget Sound for thirty years. Surely, this landmark could withstand a move.

My husband, George, and I had been married three years and were living in Sedro Woolley where he was a teacher. It surprised him when I said, "I want the house."

"And move to Whidbey Island?"

"Yes, you can find a teaching job in Oak Harbor."

After thinking about it, he talked with the school superintendent, who said they needed teachers. George was also concerned that we'd have to buy land. When we told my dad, he quickly said, "I'll sell you a piece of my property on Monroe Landing Road and you pay me when you can."

We talked with a house-moving company in Langley. The owner figured our house weighed about forty-five tons, but he could move it. My cousins, Margaret and Roy Peterson, bought Uncle Ed's house and made arrangements with the same contractor. The houses would be carried on the same barge.

Early in August 1958, the contractor came with his three-man crew and two beat-up old trucks. They brought lumber, dollies, a bulldozer and other equipment. The workers punched through the cement walls of the basement with jack-hammers and inserted huge wood beams through the holes under the house. They jacked up the beams and put dollies under them. The contractor checked the tide table and told us the houses would be taken to the beach on Saturday and loaded onto the barge the next morning, September 28.

Our house ready for the move

Petersons' house was moved from Uncle Ed's farm down the road past our house on its way to Weidenbach Beach, commonly known as West Beach. Then it was time to move our house. We watched as the truck pulled it away from the foundation and down the gravel road one-quarter mile to the beach.

The men had used bulldozers to push rocks, sand and logs to construct a ramp topped with heavy planks. A large tugboat maneuvered the barge to the beach, and pushed its stern up to the ramp. A small tug kept the barge from drifting side to side. My cousins' house was pulled onto the barge. As the sun disappeared behind the Olympic Mountains, our house was settled on the barge.

The journey from West Beach began the next

morning. Excitement grew as neighbors and friends joined us on Deception Pass Bridge on that spectacular September day. The deep green water sparkled in the sun. Eagles perched in the evergreen trees on the sheer rock cliffs. We stood along the bridge railing and looked to the west. People called out, "Here they come! Here they come!" as the tugs and barge came around the West Beach point to North Beach.

We leaned over the railing and watched as the tug pulled our houses through the churning whirlpools under the bridge.

So far below, the tugs and houses looked like toys as they continued the journey past the old ferry landing at Hoypus Point.

They passed Cornet Bay into Saratoga Passage, past Dugualla Bay, around Strawberry Point and Oak Harbor. After passing around Blowers Bluff, they reached Penn Cove during low tide and anchored overnight, a safe distance from the beach, to wait for high tide the next day.

Curious folks gathered with us at Penn Cove beach in the morning. Women watched their children build sandcastles and wade in the water. Men stood around with hands in their pockets debating whether the makeshift bridge of piers and planks would support the heavy loads and if the old trucks could pull the houses up the steep grass hill.

A ramp of logs and planks had been built on the beach below Kennedys' house. As the tide came in, the big tug pushed the barge to the beach. The truck pulling Peterson's house drove over the ramp, crossed Penn Cove Road, and started up field at the base of the hill. It continued up through Van de

Werforsts' alfalfa field and finally to Peterson's property about a quarter-mile south of the Blue Fox Drive-in Theatre on the west-side of Monroe Landing Road.

By late afternoon, the barge floated higher in the slack water and the men started moving our house. As the truck reached the ramp to begin its descent to Penn Cove Road, George pointed out that a wheel on one of the dollies wobbled. What would happen if it came off?

The men stopped the truck, examined the dolly and motioned to the driver to keep going. The truck slowly moved forward. After moving a few feet, the wheel fell off and rolled down onto the sand. The truck kept moving. The dolly with three wheels miraculously held and our house started on its final journey up through the fields. It crossed Monroe Landing Road onto our property located in the John Condra Donation Land Claim.

A worker drove the truck over the planks which had been laid on four wood beams across the hole dug for the basement. The movers had done their work, and the house would sit there perched on the beams through the fall and winter.

Anxious to look inside the house, we climbed a ladder to the porch, and went into the kitchen. As we walked through each room, we looked for cracks in the plaster and chimneys. It all looked good.

Everett Brothers Construction Company began work on the foundation during the fall. After they constructed forms for the walls, they filled them with concrete and poured the basement floor. They brought load after load of concrete. After they removed the forms, they dumped truckloads of gravel a short distance from the house. George and I spent many hours filling a wheelbarrow with gravel and dumping it to fill the space around the concrete walls.

We cleaned the walls, floors, cupboards and closets throughout the house, and planned that someday we would paint and wallpaper, and get new linoleum in the kitchen and bathroom. We would also buy new light fixtures, and eventually hire a carpenter to build kitchen cabinets around the sink and stove. Talking about future plans made the work go faster. In April 1959, we moved into our house. We were home!

House set on the pilings after the big trip on the barge. Next to the house is the concrete garage where we lived for eight months while getting the house ready.

The White House on Ducken Road

I watched the yellow convertible car come up Ducken Road and turn into the driveway. The driver cut the noiseless engine and rolled to a stop where I stood leaning on my walking stick. The reporter from the *Island Times* took off his sunglasses, reached his hand out through the open window, and said, "Jess Porter." I shook it and said, "Sam Morry." I judged him to be about forty or so, half my age. I stepped back as he opened the door, lifted out his long legs, and stood beside me on the gravel driveway. I looked up at his freckled face topped off with a bushel of carrot-red hair.

"So, you want to know about the house?"

"And the barn," he said. "There's a group of women who want the farm to be designated as an Historical Landmark."

"I guess you want to know the whole story."

"That's the idea."

He had called the day before asking if I could tell him the history of the big white house on Ducken Road. I stroked my bearded chin while contemplating for a bit. I caressed the smooth hood of the car. "This reminds me of a Volkswagen."

"It's the Volkswagen Beetle."

I laughed, "It's kinda small for a big fellow like you. I used my grandpa's VW Bug when I went to college in Bellingham."

"Western Washington University?"

"Back then we called it a college." I leaned into

the car and felt the leather seat. "Haven't had a
chance to ride in one of these electric cars, and I've
never ridden in a car with no top. After we talk you
can take me for a ride." Looking up at him I grinned
and asked, "That'a bargain?"

"Well, sure, why not?" We shook hands again.
"That's a bargain," he said.

"Okay, come with me."

"Just a sec," he said. He reached into his car. I
saw him pull out a black case, a laptop. I knew what
it was because almost everyone in my family had
one. Using my stick, I started down the slope toward
the barn. After he caught up with me, we sat on the
old milk stand where the filled cans used to be set out
for the Darigold truck to pick up in the mornings.
Darigold had quit coming for milk a few years ago
when the last dairy farm on the island either sold out
or started raising grains or beef cattle.

He opened his laptop. He typed *June 14, 2019,
The Old Farm on Ducken Road, Interview with Mr.
Sam Morry.*

I grinned and said, "Okay, you're in for a story.
My grandparents bought this land in the late 1890's.
There was a little house on that hillside just down
from Monkey Hill Road. That's where they lived and
where my father was born. All this land," I used my
arm to show him the spread, "was covered with trees
like those you see down in Deception Pass
Park—cedar, Doug fir, salal, sword ferns—all over
this property."

Jess asked, "So this property all the way up to
Monkey Hill Road belonged to your family?"

"Yeah, they cleared all this land. It wasn't easy.

It took a lot of hard work, but then they were young and weren't afraid of work. The men used those long cross-cut saws. If you take a walk around in the woods up on the hill," I pointed with my stick, "you might find stumps with the wedges cut out of them."

I waited to give him time to get it all down, but he typed about as fast as I talked. "There was a time when my grandpa walked nine miles or more into Oak Harbor. There weren't any roads. Everyone walked on Indian trails. He worked out on Maylor's Point clearing land, stayed there during the week and then came home on weekends to work with Grandma. He earned money that way so he could build the barn and house."

"When did he build the barn?"

"That would've been in 1904. Grandma's brother-in-law helped him."

"Okay if we go in and have a look around?"

"Sure." I watched him close his case and then we slid off the milk stand. I stood up and stretched my arms, picked up my stick, and we walked to the barn and went in.

He had put his sunglasses back on, but now he took them off so he could see in the shadows. "Wow!" he said, looking up to the top.

I said, "All those support poles were made from the cedar that grew down in a marshy area. Cedars like lots of water."

We walked into the gangway that divided the barn. He looked and looked some more. The barn showed its age—cracks between boards where wind whistled through on stormy nights. "The roof has all hand-split cedar shakes," I told him. "The stalls on the right side were for the draft horses. All their harnesses," I nodded to a far wall, "hung from wooden pegs."

He looked up at the lofts. I said, "Loose hay was brought in from the fields on wagons and they used tongs to take it up to a track that ran the length of the barn. Men working up there on the lofts pulled a rope to open the tongs to let the hay drop. They used their forks to toss it to the sides."

I slid a door open into the milking area on the other side of the gangway. There were enough wood stanchions for twelve cows to put their heads through. Each stanchion had a wooden box for the cow's grain. The cows stood on a plank floor raised above the ground. "Cows are like people."

He looked at me. "Oh, how's that?"

"Did you ever notice when people come into a meeting or such, they sit in the same place? Well cows always go to the same stanchion." I laughed, "Yep, they like their own space."

He used his cell phone to take pictures as he kept looking at this and that—the old stanchions, the gutter for the cows' manure. He opened his laptop again to write down my answers to his questions. How many cows? Where did they get water? What's this? What's that?

I said, "I guess you've never been on a farm."

"Nope, I grew up in Detroit and stayed there until a year ago. After getting a divorce, I came out to Washington. I don't know much about farms."

We turned when we heard squeals of laughter.

I said, "Looks like some of the family have come to pick cherries and have a picnic." We started out of the barn as kids from ages six to twelve came skipping and running to the barn.

"Hi, Uncle Sam," they called. I put my arms out and caught little Sal. She gave me a hug and squirmed out of my arms. I laughed and said, "These are my niece's and nephew's kids. They're anxious to swing and play their games."

"Okay if I take a few pictures of them?"

"Go ahead. I'm sure they'll make a few faces for you."

After he had taken pictures of the kids climbing ladders up to the loft and swinging in the gangway on a rope hanging from the peak of the barn, we went out.

We heard a boy call out "Let's play Kick the Can." I said, "That's one of their favorite games."

We started walking up through the orchard of cherry, apple, and pear trees, some close to a hundred years old. We heard my sister and nieces laughing as they spread tablecloths on the old wood picnic tables scattered beneath the trees. Their chatter stopped and they looked up at us. "This is a reporter from the *News Times*," I said. "I'm going to show him the house." I reached above me for a handful of Royal Anne cherries and told Jess to help himself.

We walked around to the back porch of the two-story house. I didn't mention that it needed a coat of paint. He could figure that out himself.

"How old is it?" he asked.

"Grandpa and a guy named Bunnell built it in 1910."

"That puts it at 112 years old."

"Guess that's about right. The family had to sell

the farm a few years ago. The owner has plans for the barn and the house."

We walked up onto the porch. I opened the kitchen door.

The old wood cookstove had been replaced with a modern stove, and gone was the wooden bench where the kids sat during the big family Thanksgiving dinners. Behind a door in the corner a flight of stairs led to the bedrooms.

We walked into the dining room. All the woodwork, the window frames and doors, and the fireplace had the original brown stain beneath a coat of white paint. I looked for the picture of the lone wolf in the snow, but it was gone. Jess stooped and looked under the table. He said, "I've always liked these oak tables with the claw feet."

Although he didn't need to, he dipped his head as he entered the living room, a comfortable looking room with a cushioned couch and chairs.

Gone was my grandpa's old Victrola. Gone were the large oval-framed portrait photographs of my grandpa, grandma, and great-grandma that had hung side by side on one wall.

I opened the front door, and as we stepped out onto the porch, he commented, "Pretty fancy etching in that glass door. I'd like a picture." I stepped off the porch and waited while he took the photo.

"I think that about does it," he said. He closed his laptop and we walked to his car. "Well, sir," he held out his hand, "it's been a pleasure." We shook hands and he opened the Beetle's door.

I said, "Are you forgetting something?"

"Uh, no," he looked in the back seat. "I've got

my laptop."

"A bargain's a bargain," I said.

"Uh, oh, yes sir." He grinned. "A bargain's a bargain." I followed him around to the passenger side.

Seated on the soft leather seat, I looked at all the buttons and gadgets. Then we were moving, but I hadn't heard the roar of an engine. He drove out of the yard up to Monkey Hill Road. He turned right onto Troxell, then onto the old Tea and Coffee Road. I could feel the wind and held on to my hat for a quiet ride to Highway 20 and then up Ducken Road. As I got out, I said, "I'll be looking for your story in the paper. It better be a good one."

Chris and Margareta Weidenbach, who were my grandparents, cleared the land and raised their four children on the farm until 1915 when they purchased a farm on West Beach. Their eldest daughter, Anna, and her husband, Ben Ducken, farmed the land on Ducken road for many years. The present owners transformed the barn into a place for entertainment events and weddings. They have plans for the house. I hope the farm will one day be designated as a historical landmark.

A Smith Prairie Landmark

During my growing-up years, I heard about the swell times my Kellogg ancestors had in their Smith Prairie home. From those stories and one picture of the large colonial-style house, I'm imagining how it might have been—all fiction. Circa 1890's.

"Giddy-up! Giddy-up!" William flicked the reins on the pony's back. The hollow clip-clop, clip-clop sound of Jack's iron shoes hitting rocks in the hardpan clay road broke the silence of the still night. In the April night sky, filled with stars in the Milky Way, an almost full moon shone down on the young couple in William's black buggy.

Married just an hour before in the parsonage of the Methodist minister, Emma and William were on their way to his sister's home on Smith Prairie where they would spend two nights. On the second morning, they would board the schooner, *Valaria,* captained by William's brother-in-law, James.

"Sweetheart, Emma dear, do you like your new name?"

She giggled, "Mrs. William Montgomery Crandell, with an emphasis on Mrs."

"So be it," William laughed. He flicked the reins urging Jack into a faster trot.

The eighteen-year-old bride snuggled into the Friendship quilt made especially for this occasion by her friend, Mary. Emma would take the quilt with her on the schooner on their way to San Francisco.

As they approached the Kellogg home, light

emanated from the windows on the first and second floors. William said, "Looks like Elizabeth has lights in every window, even the cupola." He halted Jack by the hitching post.

A black Newfoundland dog barked and dashed off the porch to meet them. James stepped out onto the broad veranda to quiet his dog, Tige. Elizabeth joined him along with their sixteen-year-old twin daughters, Mary and Ruth, and sons Henry, eighteen, Joseph, fourteen, and Robert, ten. The girls scurried off the porch, running and skipping down the sloping lawn to the buggy. "Emma, we've been waiting for you! Uncle William, you took so long!"

James called, "Henry will take Jack to the barn and unhitch him." He turned to his son, "Make sure he has water, and close the gate."

"Yeah, Dad, I know," said Henry as he walked toward the buggy. "Hi, Uncle Will."

William handed the reins to him. "He could use a rubdown, Henry, if you don't mind." Then he walked around the cart to Emma. Putting his hands around her slender waist, he lifted his bride up and out of the seat and started to set her down on the grass.

"Oh, my new shoes!" she cried out.

With a swift move, William gathered her into his arms. She put her arms around his neck and kissed his cheek above the line of his red beard. He walked up to the porch and set her down by Elizabeth. "Emma, I'm so happy for you and Will," said Elizabeth, "and for me. I've always wanted a sister."

The men shook hands. James said, "This calls for a bit of Apple Jack. Come on in. He turned the

white china knob and held open the tall door made of
eighteen panes of glass. James motioned for Will to
go into the parlor leaving the women to chat on the
porch. As they entered, William whistled, "Whoo!
What's going on?"

"Come on, Will, you expect the fellas to give you
a chivari, don't you? I remember you taking part in a
few of them."

"Guess I didn't think it would happen here in
your house." The men stood by the massive stone
fireplace sipping their Apple Jack.

James said, "It doesn't matter to those
scallywags. They're out to get you. However,
Elizabeth figures if she offers the fellows food and
merriment, they'll forget about any tomfoolery and
won't be so mean to you. She directed the boys all
day on setting up tables and such. I stayed in my
study, didn't want to get involved."

The boys had rolled the floral carpet up against
the inner wall, revealing the worn but polished floor
of Whidbey Island fir. Chairs had been arranged
around the perimeter of the room. White linen cloths
covered a long makeshift table. Two crystal
kerosene-lit chandeliers hung above it. Large framed
mirrors on the walls reflected light from tall candles
set on tables in front of the windows. Elizabeth had
sent the girls out to gather wildflowers blooming on
the prairie fields and to cut pink-budded
rhododendrons growing along the edge of the woods.
She had arranged the flowers in tall urns in the
corners of the room.

As the two women went through the opened
glass doors, Emma exclaimed, "What is all this? Oh

my, Elizabeth, are we having a party?"

"Yes, we are, dear!" Elizabeth answered. James offered them a drink, but they refused the Apple Jack.

Emma looked at the decorated table. Vases of blue lupine, white daisies and Indian Paintbrush in silver vases graced the table. She admired Elizabeth's fine china and goblets. "Oh my, you did this for us?" She turned and gave her new sister-in-law a hug. "You are so kind."

Elizabeth said, "Let's go up to your bedroom, Emma. You need to rest and freshen up before the rowdies arrive."

"Who are they?"

"Word got out to Will's friends that you would be staying here, and of course they want to chivari you. I've invited them for a wedding feast like they've never had. They'll forget all about playing tricks on you."

Following Elizabeth up the staircase, Emma used her index finger to trace the pattern in the maroon and gold textured wallpaper. "I love your beautiful house. Someday Will and I will have a nice home."

Elizabeth said, "Yes, you will. My brother is a good carpenter. Joseph and Robert brought your luggage up to the east corner bedroom. You might wake up to a brilliant pink sunrise."

"That would be delightful. A good omen for Will and me."

Elizabeth heard the grandfather clock chime nine. "Goodness, I need to check how everything's going in the kitchen. You rest, dear. I'll send Will up to get you." Elizabeth left and bustled down the stairs.

Mixed aromas greeted her as she opened the kitchen door. "It smells wonderful in here! How are we doing, Millie?" she asked the fifty-year-old widow who helped in the kitchen whenever Elizabeth and James had a party.

"Everything is ready. Just you relax now." She looked at Elizabeth. "That's a stylish new gown you're wearing," she said, scrutinizing the large puffed sleeves and bell-shaped long skirt that emphasized Elizabeth's small corseted waist. The pattern for the dress had been ordered from a fashion magazine featuring the latest styles.

Elizabeth fussed around checking the different dishes—corn pudding, canned green beans from their garden, smoked salmon, fermented pickles from her crock, the Sally Lunn cake she had baked, Parker House rolls and more. "Everything looks grand, Millie. Be sure to put the red apple in the roasted pig's mouth," Elizabeth reminded, as she walked through the swinging door into the great room.

Folks arrived in buggies from far and near to join in the frivolity at James and Elizabeth's home. Henry and Joseph helped the guests with their horses. Elizabeth welcomed them into the house. After everyone had been seated, James stood at the head of the table and touched his fork to a crystal goblet. Chatter stopped. James raised his glass to the bride and groom seated at the opposite end. "Hear! Hear! To the bride and groom. To love, laughter, and happily ever after. Will and Emma, your fairy tale is just beginning. Congratulations!" James sat down with a satisfied look as guests clapped and shouted out good wishes to the young newlyweds.

After everyone had eaten their fill and the men had drunk the last drop of Apple Jack, Elizabeth motioned to John Knight who then brought out his fiddle, a signal that dancing would soon commence. The women helped clear away the dishes. As planned, Mary and Ruth took away the vases of flowers. Elizabeth and Millie gathered the linen table cloths and napkins, and the men took out the tables. John Knight started everyone dancing with James's favorite Irish jig. The Smith Prairie house was filled with fun and laughter. All thoughts of playing tricks on Will and Emma had been forgotten as dancing continued until the wee hours of the morning before the sky turned pink.

Kellogg's Smith Prairie house near Coupeville, Whidbey Island. Built between 1863 and 1866. Albert Kellogg holding Anna, Dr. Isaac Dillon, Marie, Alice, Edith holding Chester, and Dillon. Photo taken in the Spring of 1889.

My great-grandfather, Dr. John Coe Kellogg, aka "The Canoe Doctor," took a Donation Land Claim at Admiralty Head in 1854. He bought the Smith Prairie land in 1862 or '63. The family lived in a small, old cabin until the grand square house was ready sometime between 1864 and 1866. It was located at the present intersection of Keystone Road and Patmore Road near the Naval Out Lying Field. The house was sold to John Le Sourd in 1900. It burned to the ground in 1911.

"The earliest settler on the prairie seems to have been Rev. Joseph S. Smith, who came to Oregon shortly after Marcus Whitman, arriving on the island prior to 1853. He took up a Donation Claim of one square mile, and afterwards, was sent to Washington, D.C. as a delegate to Congress from Oregon Territory." –Flora Pearson Engle's Diary Recollections of Early Days on Whidbey Island, *published by the Island County Historical Society.*

Mysteries at Monroe Landing

"Mitch, I want you to see what's going on down on the beach."

"Tell me about it. What's going on?"

"No, I want you to see for yourself. Come on Mitch. You haven't been here for a while. I would've called you when I first noticed it, but then the pandemic started. COVID-19 scared everybody half to death. You should see it before it all disappears. You being the climatologist, and all the global warming talk going on, you should be able to shed a little light on it."

Mitch checked his datebook. "Well, okay, Dan. Saturday."

"Good. We'll have a low tide about 1:30. Meet me at the boat ramp."

I come to Coupeville, the second-oldest town in WA state, and find Toby's Tavern in an old mercantile building built in the 1890's. As I enjoy a bowl of mussels, fresh from the waters of Penn Cove, I look across the cove toward the boat landing at the bottom of Monroe Landing Road. I know about the Indian potlatch house on the west side of the boat ramp and the Indian burial ground to the east. I wonder what Danny is all fired up about.

Driving the scenic route on Madrona Road, I look down and see a hundred or so mussel rafts. I pass a landmark, the Captain Whidbey Inn, the former Whid-Isle Inn.

Captain Whidbey Inn, circa 1907

After passing Kennedy's Lagoon, I see another landmark, a two-story red building, the first courthouse constructed in 1855. Then I turn onto Highway 20, and glance up the hill at the San de Fuca Schoolhouse built in 1907.

San de Fuca Schoolhouse

I take a right at the old San de Fuca Fire Station, and drive on the hilly Penn Cove Road along the bluff. I slow down and marvel at the view. Spectacular! No clouds in the expansive blue sky, glistening water at ebb tide and I remember playing on the sandy beach by the old apple trees.

As I park, get out, and stretch, Danny comes up, slaps me on the back and then, surprise, he gives me a bear hug.

"Yeah, it's good to see you, too, cousin." With hands in my pockets, I follow Danny down to the cracked concrete ramp, and we look west.

"Remember when we dug in the middens across from the Monroe-Kennedy house*? We hoped to find something left from the Indian potlatch house."

The potlatch house, circa 1905. Twenty-seven canoes came from the surrounding villages.

"Yeah, I remember." I look across at the boats docked at the Coupeville Wharf. "Okay, now what's going on that you really want to show me?"

"Erosion. That's what's going on."

"That's been going on for years."

"Yeah, but not so fast as the past couple."

Walking east over rocks and mussels trapped in dried seaweed leaving the mark of the last high tide, I'm surprised when I see a deep channel between piles of driftwood behind a hill of sand. "Wow! A big change."

"Look over here." I follow Danny to a structure of rocks cemented together with rebar. I guess it's about eight feet long, two feet wide and six feet tall. Questions pop into my head and need to be answered. When and for what purpose was this built?

"Remember, Mitch, when we used to play work-up baseball down here? This wasn't exposed. It was covered with grass and brush. My kids rode their horses right over the top of it. I've been watching the soil sluff off, especially since the big storm we had a few weeks ago. We've lost fifteen to twenty feet of land that had been covered with soil and vegetation."

"Yeah, I remember. So, who built it?"

"I've asked around, but no luck. The only thing I can figure out is that it was built for guys who fished here, to tie up their boats. Dad told me there were summer cabins** here in the 1930's."

We thought for a minute. "Yeah, you're probably right, unless it was part of a wharf for the Mosquito Fleet boats. They made frequent stops up and down the island to deliver stuff and pick up produce. Maybe you were too young, but Dad used to tell us that when he was a kid, Grandpa delivered eggs and potatoes to a dock."

"What gets me, is how did so much soil accumulate over the structure and all around here between the time it was built and when we used to play down here? It's sure a mystery."

I adjusted my Mariners cap. "It beats me, Danny." I point east toward the Cascades. "I know there's an Indian burial ground farther up the channel."

"Not anymore, the graves were all dug up and the remains taken away a few years ago. All but one."

"Why is that?"

"Guess they didn't dig enough." Danny pushed a rock with his foot. "I came down a few days ago and happened to meet Ginger. She's an anthropologist from Minnesota who hoped to see the gray whales, but look what she found instead." Danny took a worn piece of paper from his wallet. He unfolded it carefully to reveal a photo. "I've been showing it to everyone."

"That's a beauty. Did she take it with her?"

"Nope. She called the sheriff. The coroner came and took it away." Danny folded the paper and put it into his wallet. "I sure wish I could figure out how that rock structure got covered up with all that dirt, enough that grass, rosebushes and other brush could grow over it."

"Well, Dan, I'm sorry I can't help you. Guess it'll remain a mystery and eventually disappear with the tides."

* The Monroe-Kennedy house was built in 1899.
**In the early 1930's, Al Olsen built a half-dozen fishing cottages and a small store at Monroe Landing on Penn Cove and called it Winono Beach. (Thank you to Rick Castellano, Island County Historical Museum, for sharing this information.)

Sandra McGillivray Ortgies

Sandra McGillivray Ortgies was born in British Columbia and grew up in West Vancouver by the sea. Moving to San Francisco where she met Don was the start of rewarding years of family travel with the USAF, stateside and in Europe. While English was Sandra's favorite subject at Texas Lutheran University, it wasn't until she enrolled in journalism electives and sold her first travel article to a Northwest magazine that she was hooked! Short stories, articles, and poetry remain her writing focus. As much as Sandra and Don enjoy their continued travels, they are always happy to come home to Whidbey Island and their Coupeville community.

Ben and Frankie: LifE

"What if…?"

Frankie sat behind the bougainvillea hedge at the corner of Orange and Third Streets, sipping a glass of Chardonnay in the California sun, willing her thoughts to point her in the right direction; any direction would at least be a start. The corner bordered a large RV site with lush grass and multicolored petunias edging a paved pad and concrete patio. An onsite tree dropped its fuzzy catkins like gliding caterpillars onto the picnic table.

"What if?" Frankie said it again…louder, as if more volume would call up an idea.

Ben latched the screen door on their travel trailer and strolled across the patio. "Hey, darlin', there's a worm in your wine."

Frankie fished the catkin out of her glass and flicked it off her fingers at him.

"That pickup line works pretty well for you, cowboy?"

"Beats, 'Is this seat taken?' every time."

Ben slid across the picnic table bench with a quick glance at the legal pad covered with sketches of house plans and doodles. "I don't see a single 'once upon a time' in all this graffiti, Frankie."

"My usual 'what if' prompt isn't working. And here we are on vacation…best chance for a fiction idea to come leaping out at me. You know, I'm tired of the pressure of investigative reporting. I'd really like the freedom of writing more fiction for a change, more travel articles, and something totally different.

We could team-write an 'agony column,' as long as I get to edit your comments."

"You don't think my positive suggestions… along the lines of, 'Listen up, lighten up, and grow up'…would be appreciated?" Ben uncapped a beer and opened the bag of almonds he'd gathered in the grove across the road earlier that morning.

"Frankie, I remember Dad saying, 'Life is a four-letter word, and half of it, is *if*.' You've got some time to go in all sorts of iffy directions this month."

"But that's it, Ben. While we actually get a generous amount of time off over all, a couple of weeks at a time to devote to fiction before getting back to work is not enough. Assignment deadlines are riding along right now." Frankie leapt up, pacing around the picnic table. "Let's retire…there, I've said it!

"The more I go over plans for our new house, the less it appeals to me. Not the house; it's exactly what we want…just not until we've traveled more, experienced some in-between time, I guess."

Ben sat quietly, observing the pacing and listening intently to Frankie's proposed plan. She handed him the legal pad drawings. "Don't you think we could always do this? I mean, we've got the view lot on the west side of Whidbey. It'll wait for us. We don't have to build right away." She reached for the almonds, drew a deep breath, and went on.

"Say we took off for three years and roamed with an RV? We'd need something bigger than this trailer…maybe a motorhome…and we could tow the Mini Cooper. Leaving our Coupeville community for an extended time would be the hardest part, but we could store our belongings and return to visit Whidbey at its best, when all the summer festivals are going on.

"Even with the limited amount of time we've had for longer trips…we've really enjoyed our travels, and I think it's partly because we know we're coming home to Coupeville. That's the only way I want to see Whidbey in our rearview mirror: knowing that we're coming back each time. I can only imagine how we'd be after an extended journey: probably have to take inventory of all our favorite places, from one end of the island to the other, as soon as we landed."

Fresnel Lens at Admiralty Head Lighthouse

Frankie slid across the bench to sit beside Ben again. "You know how we are now at the end of a road trip…approaching Coupeville on the ferry from Port Townsend, running up to the bow with Rudi barking because he seems to know we're almost home. We can't wait to see Admiralty Head Lighthouse welcoming us home. Maybe it's because we worked there as tour guides when we first came to Whidbey, and had to get to know the lighthouse to relate its landmark history to visitors. I can still see the lighthouse Fresnel lens on display, shining like a jewel.

"The lighthouse and the bridge are the island landmark stars, but Georgia Gerber's bronze sculpture of *The Boy and His Dog* in Langley is my favorite."

Frankie reached for her reading glasses and pulled a West Coast map from the travel file, unfolding it on the picnic table. "There's a story a mile post out there, Ben, and I want to have a go at them. Just imagine the freedom of being on the road full time…stopping where and when we want."

"Wow! You've really been thinking about this, haven't you?" Ben grinned at her, and took a swallow of his beer while he considered the possibility.

"It could work! With the computer, I can take care of a lot of details from the road, while you're doing your Charles Kuralt's *On the Road* thing. We'd likely see more of our family and friends traveling around. And, you're right; the stories are out there. Remember Angela and Joe?"

Frankie smiled, recalling a memorable vacation

in South Texas where they'd arrived in the early evening at an RV park on the Gulf Coast.

The owner was ready to close, but took them into the office where they registered for the night. "We're almost full. I'm going to have to put you over there near that beat-up Winnebago. Just so you know, Joe and Angela have been here for a while. They're broke, and I finally gave them gas money to get them out of here in the morning. In earlier times, they'd have been tagged as Gypsies. He's a farrier, and she makes jewelry she'll try to sell you. Have a good night."

While Ben got to work hooking up the electrical, cable, water, and sewer connections, Frankie set up the inside appliances. Their dachshund, Rudi, came out from beside the bed dragging his leash behind him, more than ready to go for a walk after a long travel day.

The faded Winnebago towed an enclosed utility trailer. Joe was using a hand pump to top off the tires while Angela was up on a stepladder washing the windshield. Three small children chased kittens and loaded toys into the old motorhome. Preparations were clearly underway to leave.

After Ben and Frankie finished their taco supper, they sat outside to catch the sunset over the Gulf of Mexico. Angela walked directly over to them. "I am Angela, and he is my husband, Joe," she said, pointing back to where Joe was still working on the motorhome. "We are going to Florida where Joe will find work at the race tracks."

"We're Frankie and Ben. Please sit down." Frankie had anticipated a visit, and poured another glass of iced tea. She gestured at their picnic table.

"I have my jewelry to show you," said Angela, splaying her hands where turquoise rings adorned all ten of her tanned fingers.

No hard sell here, thought Ben. *Take it or leave it.*

"I like this one," said Frankie. "May I try it on?" Gauging Angela's finger sizes, she pointed to a silver ring with a small turquoise stone.

"Twenty dollars for you," said Angela removing the ring as she sat down, and started to drink her tea.

"Tell us about your travels," said Frankie, sitting opposite Angela.

Does this Angela person know that she is about to be interviewed? thought Ben. He knew Frankie wouldn't be able to resist this story.

"Excuse me one moment while I go inside and get your money," said Frankie, admiring her new ring.

Frankie always kept a hundred dollars in the trailer. She had grown up with parents who had the same amount of cash on hand. She reached into her trailer stash and tucked a twenty-dollar bill into an envelope…hesitated, and then added the other four twenties. She returned to the picnic table at the same time Joe stepped off a romance cover, swept his hand through his dark curls, and sauntered over to join them. Staring straight into Angela's eyes, Frankie handed her the envelope.

"Thank you," said Angela, zipping the envelope into her denim jacket pocket as she introduced Joe, then resuming their conversation.

When Ben and Frankie got up around seven the

next morning and raised the shades, the Winnebago was gone. Frankie glanced at her right hand where she'd placed the little silver and turquoise ring.

As they carried their breakfast out to the picnic table, Frankie reached back to close the trailer door. Tied to the handle with a piece of red raffia was a silver bracelet.

"I wonder if they made it all the way from Texas to Florida," said Frankie, handing Ben her wine glass while gathering the writing pad and sketches of house plans.

"At least they had a plan," Ben added, getting to his feet. "That's it, I guess: Have a goal, or some reason to go in a certain direction, but be ready to change course at any time." Frankie nodded...Ben was on board with the idea, and that's all that mattered to her.

"Lots of decisions and arrangements to put into play when we get back to Whidbey this time, but we agree that taking off looking for adventure and places to explore will be the next chapter in our lives." Ben hugged her close. "Do you really think we're flexible enough for life on the road, Frankie?"

"No *if's* about it, Ben. We can do this!"

The Salish Sea Connection
And Mostly Endearing Similarities of Whidbey Island, Washington and West Vancouver, British Columbia

How lucky am I, after all our Air Force moves, to have come almost full circle back to West Vancouver, B.C. where I grew up, and now to live on Whidbey Island, where my husband, Don, and I recently celebrated our fifty-fifth wedding anniversary…and where we'll likely end up. At least that's what we're counting on.

Whidbey Island has been our home for almost thirty years. We have lived here longer than anywhere else. West Vancouver, where I lived my first twenty-three years, is a familiar back-up in many shared ways, and the Salish Sea connection between my two countries emphasizes this bond. The Salish Sea encompasses Puget Sound, the San Juan Islands, and the Strait of Georgia, spanning from Olympia, Washington, in the south to Campbell River, B.C., in the north, and west through the Strait of Juan de Fuca to Neah Bay, Washington.

Whidbey is an island, and while West Vancouver is not, it might as well be with the waters of Burrard Inlet on three sides, and Hollyburn Mountain barricading the fourth. Most access to West Vancouver is over Lions Gate Bridge (completed in 1938) or across the inlet by ferry. The same is true for Whidbey Island via Deception Pass Bridge (completed in 1935) and more government ferries. In both locations, timing and patience with full ferry sailings and stalled bridge traffic lanes need to be taken into consideration in making plans.

Whidbey has the Clinton to Mukilteo ferry, which is a commuter route to Seattle, and also the Coupeville to Port Townsend crossing. Taking the half-hour "sea cruise" to Port Townsend makes a great side trip for visitors to Whidbey Island...no car is necessary, as shops, parks, and restaurants line the main street where the ferry lands.

West Vancouver has Horseshoe Bay ferry terminal with sailings to Nanaimo on Vancouver Island, Sechelt on the "Sunshine Coast" peninsula, and Bowen Island, a twenty-minute ferry ride from Horseshoe Bay.

At sea in any type of craft is where I want to be. Growing up, the craft was an inflatable life raft that Dad had picked up at the Army and Navy Store after the war, and we'd paddle along the West Van shoreline on Burrard Inlet. Then, after first settling here on the beach at Mutiny Bay on Whidbey, Don gave me a kayak. With a nod to Jimmy Buffett, I am the daughter of a daughter of a sailor man, and we three wanted our touchstone sea at the ready...in sight, sound, and smell.

The bridges and ferries are portals to all sorts of adventures and reunions. But we return to these favored places, Whidbey or West Van, with a deep feeling of contentment, often expressed with a "whew" after dealing with Seattle or Vancouver traffic. Home again!

The Salish Sea is the way by which all early settlers landed here on Whidbey and in West

Vancouver. Early days on Whidbey Island saw rustic cabins being built, sometimes two or three on one lot with iffy property lines for vacationing Seattleites. The same was true in West Vancouver; tents and cabins bordering the pebbly beaches…summer places for those coming over on small passenger ferries from Vancouver. The summer communities that sprang up were gradually rebuilt with full-time homes taking advantage of the captivating views in both locales.

Lush backdrops of evergreens and Madrona trees on Whidbey, called Arbutus trees in West Van, edge gardens that grow abundantly alongside wild blackberries in our shared oceanic climate. B.C. friends arriving for late summer visits would check out a local blackberry patch near the Mutiny Bay Boat Launch, and bake blackberry pies for our potluck suppers. West Vancouver blackberry patches meant extra spending money as we neighborhood kids picked and sold them for ten cents a basket.

The Salish Sea parallels the West Vancouver shoreline, while surrounding Whidbey Island like a moat. Beaches from Clinton to Deception Pass provide varied opportunities to be in touch with this shared far-reaching seamark, whether by taking an invigorating swim, wading into salty waves throwing smooth skip stones, hunting agates, or kayaking with the chance of a seal, all big eyes and whiskers, popping up beside your kayak. The same is true of beach coves in West Vancouver, from Ambleside to Horseshoe Bay.

Situated in both locales are the landmark

lighthouses: Admiralty Head Lighthouse on Whidbey near Coupeville, and Point Atkinson Lighthouse off Marine Drive on the way to Horseshoe Bay. Both are located in beautiful parks, treasured in their communities, and seasonally open for visitors.

If an international day trip following the Salish Sea appeals to you, this is what we suggest you do. Board the morning Amtrak train in Mt. Vernon, Washington, that arrives in Vancouver, B.C., about noon. The train is usually on time leaving Mt. Vernon on the mainland, and we're on our way across the Skagit Valley to the coast. As we take a slow curve north at Samish Bay, one of the most scenic stretches appears: ocean-going freighters at anchor in the distance waiting their turn at the Anacortes docks, herons wading along the rocky beach intent on finding a fishy morsel, and kayaks slicing through the Salish Sea waves. The train tracks wind along the shoreline, skirting small bays, to chase through tunnels that bank the Chuckanut Drive to Bellingham. This is the last stop before Vancouver for passengers to get on or off the train. We cross the border at Peace Arch Park, Blaine, Washington, and minutes later continue at slow speed through the colorful and inviting town of White Rock, B.C., paralleling their seawall walk and Salish Sea views. There really is a huge white rock on the beach halfway through town.

Arriving in Vancouver, we take the elevated SkyTrain from the train station to where we can either take a regular bus across Lions Gate Bridge to West Vancouver, or the SeaBus from the Vancouver waterfront across the harbor to Lonsdale Quay (a smaller version of Granville Island) in North Vancouver, and then the bus to West Vancouver. We opt for the harbor catamaran almost every time.

Our first stop in the Dundarave Village section of West Vancouver is for lunch at a seaside restaurant by the pier before walking the scenic seawall with views across Burrard Inlet to Lions Gate Bridge, Stanley Park, University of British Columbia, and Point Atkinson Lighthouse. This seawall walk from Dundarave Village through Ambleside Village to the Capilano River follows the natural shoreline. It was constructed in 1967 to commemorate the Canadian Centennial. It's about a mile from Dundarave to the Ambleside area of West Van, which includes numerous shops, cafes, a fine library system, and an active museum and archives...the same amenities that contribute to making Whidbey Island such an attractive place to live.

Time tends to slip away on these mini-vacation day trips, and it's best to be back at the Amtrak station by late afternoon to guarantee a window seat on the water side of the train for the return trip to Mt. Vernon. Depending on the time of year, this relaxing sunset ride home, mostly beside the meandering Salish Sea, offers a smooth transition to our Whidbey Island lives.

Map by Terry Hansen
of Dorothy Read and Associates

Barb Bland

Barb Bland writes memoir and poetry. Her book, **Running Free**, recounts her adventures while helping Pikachu, a feral dog, become a successful family pet. She grew up in Wisconsin, studied there and in France, and met her husband teaching in Alaska. Together, they crewed on a 37 foot sailboat from Seward, Alaska to Victoria, B.C., which led to their buying a house on Whidbey Island. There, they have lived happily ever after. Barb has been an active animal volunteer, first with a wildlife rehabilitation clinic, then with WAIF, one of the first minimal-kill animal shelters in North America. Her poetry has won several awards. Her interests in animals, writing, art, photography, gardening, and travel keep her busy.

Fog

blurs
houses down the block
slides off roofs, sifts between buildings
swirls and scatters like wind-driven sand grains
twisting, tumbling in kaleidoscopic patterns

rises
from the ocean's kettle like steam
writhing upward, bending, sliding,
crouching, springing, gyrating, swaying:
running, leaping, arms outstretched, ribbons flowing

snuggles
nests in spikes of Scotch Broom along the roadside
muffles the swish, swish of passing cars
clings to eyelashes, building beads, jewels
quiet quilts of precious, evanescent moisture

The Only Call
I Didn't Answer Personally

I was in the midst of cooking for that evening's dinner party in 1988 when the phone rang.

"We just got a call that there's a flying squirrel impaled on a barbed wire fence near Dugualla Bay," Mary, the vet's wife, said.

"Darn." I hesitated. "I can't answer this one."

I was genuinely disappointed. It was the first call in my three years as a volunteer for the Wildlife Care Clinic that I couldn't respond to. Once before, when a report had come in about an injured deer just as I was about to leave home to attend a party, I phoned the hostess and said I would be late. But this party was at my own house. I was in a bind.

I was the one and only designated Search and Rescue person for the clinic, though I had always been able to enlist the aid of bystanders or people in the neighborhood when I had to bring in an animal I couldn't handle by myself.

Who could I find to answer this time? Everybody would say "I've never *done* that before" but who the hell *had*? I didn't even know we *had* flying squirrels on Whidbey Island! And we couldn't just leave the critter there to die slowly in the heat of a summer afternoon. Since most wild animal rescue attempts don't have happy endings, it would have to be someone who could deal with that possibility.

"I'll find somebody and get back to you," I told Mary.

Who do I know on the North End who's calm and levelheaded enough to tackle this?

I thought of Judy and Ted. She was an experienced dog person, and he was a crop-duster pilot. Neither was impulsive. They might be able to work together. Ted lived within two miles of the site. Judy would have to come a little farther.

I phoned each and found them at home, thank goodness. Judy agreed immediately.

"I don't know much about flying squirrels either, Ted," I began, as I glanced at the clock. It was three-ish. "All the pictures I've seen of them have been taken at night, so if this baby is nocturnal, then he or she has been out there a long time."

"You sure it's still alive?"

"No, but when it was reported to the vet within the hour, it was. I'm not even certain you can find it, although I can tell you what I know about where it is. Unless we know that the folks who report this stuff are accurate, your time can be wasted with a wild goose chase, so this has to be done out of the goodness of your heart."

Pause.

"I've found a partner for you, so you won't be all alone. Here's her phone number."

I had already told Judy what I would have done to proceed: "Lightly cover the animal's head, so it can breathe but not see -- this usually makes critters stop struggling. Wear gloves to protect yourself-- from the wire as well as possible bites and scratches. Take along wire cutters and plan to apologize to the farmer later for damaging his fence, but cut out the section with the squirrel still on it. Don't try to remove the animal from the wire yourselves. And bring along a large towel to wrap the squirrel in while you carry it to the vet's office."

"Okay. Sounds like we can give it a try."

"I'll phone the vet to let him know who's bringing it in. Please get back to me as soon as you can. Ted's house is closest if you need to call me while you're out there. I'll be standing by."

For the next hour I tried to get my own tasks done, all the while wondering: were they able to find it? Was it alive? *If* alive, was it just the membrane on either side between the ankles and wrists that the animals used to glide that might be punctured or was it the actual body of the squirrel? Would the vet be able to treat it right away or was he up to his ears in paying customers?

When my phone finally rang about 4:30, I could hear the satisfaction in Ted's voice: "It's okay. We got 'er done. Mission accomplished."

"Where was it punctured?"

"On those flaps of skin it uses to glide."

"Did the vet have to sedate it to get it off the wire?"

"No, the squirrel was so far gone and weak that just keeping his head covered was enough to manage. It was easy for the vet to slip it off the wire. The critter just couldn't do it by himself."

"So, did you give it water and something to eat to revive it?"

"Well, he took a drink, but we didn't really know what to try to feed him. He just sat on Mary's desk watching us while we watched ...until Mary opened up her desk drawer for something and found a partly unwrapped candy bar with chocolate-covered nuts. Boy, did he perk up when she offered it to him! He came back to life so fast that Judy and I took him right back and released him near the spot where we found him.

Thinking of this critter's safe return to the forests near beautiful Dugualla Bay made me feel as good as if I had been there myself.

The Blue Hole

Towering sandstone cliffs stand at attention as
a walker passes in review on the shore below.

They fortify Whidbey's West Beach from winds
    and waves of the open ocean
    funneling through the Strait from
    the Pacific into the Salish Sea.

The surge and gurgle of luscious, lapping water
    rattle stones worn smooth
    by retreating waves.

Kelp weeds, their anchor stones uprooted by the surf,
    lie tangled on the sand, marooned
    by last night's first fall storm,
    its purple clouds still heaped
    on nearby peaks and islands.

But between Point Partridge and the Navy base--
    a microclimate protected by
    the rain shadow - an onshore
    west wind has fractured the storm,

        exposing blue sky and sun,
        bathing West Beach in brilliance and
        warmth unlike its neighbors
        to the south and north.

            The Blue Hole
        where sky and sea open wide.
        A rare place on the island
         where one can view
    the   subtle   broad   blue   curvature
          of   the   earth.

The Commodore's Ball
December 17, 1983

A contentious year, 1983. Yes, that might be a good way of describing the efforts of Oak Harbor Yacht Club members to finally build their own clubhouse.

The faction that wanted to borrow funds and hire professional builders eventually bowed to those led by my husband, the Commodore, Curt Bland; the latter were determined to pay-as-we-go and use members' voluntary and quite-skilled labor without going into debt.

Now, after rushing to make the shell of a building available for the newly instigated Whidbey Island Race Week the previous July, we were facing the presentation of our first formal event, the annual Commodore's Ball.

Icy, wind-driven rain pelted the December night as my very nervous husband parked the car and we dashed through the clubhouse front door. It was around six o'clock and we had arrived an hour early to help with set-up and to be sure we were well organized. I realized that Curt's nerves were on edge because he had to lead a Change of Command in front of high-ranking retired military officers, 05s and 06s. The Navy always made a noticeable distinction between officers and enlisted men. He was himself a retired Air Force E7, and thus had never before had a command. He put a lot of pressure on himself to do this right, in front of his fellow retired military peers.

"Shit. I don't have the flags." His eyes were pleading with me as I glanced at him.

It was customary that each incoming yacht club officer receive a burgee revealing his or her rank which could then be flown on their boat beneath the yacht club burgee, which flew beneath the American flag.

"I'll go home and get them. Are they in your desk drawer?"

"I don't know. I think so."

So much for the start of a pleasant, relaxing evening, I thought, as I made for the door.

We always carried our big creampuff of a Shepherd-Husky dog, Kluane, everywhere with us in the car when we knew we would be gone from home for more than one or two hours because left at home, she was known to have destroyed pillows and we returned to a blizzard of feathers. But left in the car, she was quite placid, and I made a point of taking her out every couple hours. She greeted me with mellow thumps of her tail.

Back at home, I rummaged in a desk drawer where I knew Curt kept our American flag.

No burgees.

Now what? I couldn't return without them. And I couldn't be late. Wondering what to do, I wandered around the house several times.

There they were! On the front hall table. Hooray! *Why hadn't I seen them the first time around?*

Back to the yacht club about 6:45.

It wasn't just the retired Navy officers themselves that we had to look good for.

It was their wives.

Even though Long Dresses were no longer the latest fashion in the early '80s, the self-appointed Arbiter of Good Taste among a picky little côterie of retired wives decreed that they were the proper formal attire for this event.

I groaned, because in our attempt to pay-as-we-go in building the clubhouse, we had decided to fully finish the upper story before we got over-involved in the lower one, where the bar was. That meant that concrete dust from the not-yet-sealed lower floor would frost the hems of the ladies' long dresses. So, I decided not to wear the black one I loved and wore a red one I didn't much care for, instead. I also loaded up on all my *real* jewelry, thinking how proud all my friends in the well-to-do suburb I had grown up in would be if they knew my status on this elite occasion.

The main meeting room on the clubhouse's upper story was nicely finished with a parqueted wooden dance floor, a lovely paint and wallpaper job and classy bathrooms. However, the kitchen wasn't so great. The club's custom in the years before we had a place of our own had been to have potluck dinners. And since we couldn't yet afford a commercial kitchen, this one was really makeshift, stocked with a couple old hand-me-down household stoves and refrigerators.

The caterer we hired for this occasion brought prepared food from the nearby town of Coupeville, but planned to heat it at the club before serving.

Around seven o'clock the members gathered in their finery. The little pack of retired Navy officers' wives wearing their *de rigueur* Long Dresses stood in a corner and sneered at my friend Betty Tuck's simple and elegant pale-blue silk short dress. As if the wife of a full colonel in the Air Force was by nature inferior to the wife of a Navy captain, even though their ranks were equivalent: the length of her dress only confirmed it. The principal Arbiter of Good Taste had grown up in a small Minnesota farming town and considered herself to have hit the Big Time when she went out into the world and married a Navy helicopter pilot. Nice guy, but actually low on the pecking order of Navy pilots. HIGH enough for her, she could now hobnob with captains. Fortunately, I knew my red dress with its floor-length split skirt and matching jacket would prove acceptable to the female High Command.

By 7:15, with Curt first in line and me by his side, we led the yacht club officers and board members and their spouses past tables filled with hors-d'oeuvres, gathering tidbits on our plates before we sat together at a long table. The rest of the of members gathered in line behind us. Marie Omoth tapped me on the shoulder as she reached over me and grabbed an appetizer from my plate. "I'm *starving*," she gasped. I quickly excused her because we were old friends.

BANG! One resounding, unmistakable bang came from the kitchen at 7:25. We all heard it. As soon as talking resumed after the shocked silence, I excused myself from the table and forced myself to walk, not run, to the kitchen.

"What happened?"

"One of the stoves blew. And the other one doesn't have a temperature regulator. I'm going to have to drive back to Coupeville to heat the food," the caterer said.

"How long will that take?"

"Oh, not long. I'll be back within the hour," he breezed. "And I'll put out extra bottles of wine on the tables for everybody - my treat."

Which he did.

I returned to our table and tried to look nonchalant as I explained what the caterer said. By now, the dinners that had been heated before the explosion were being served at our table.

The better part of an hour crept by. Curt felt a sudden rap on his shoulder, turned and stood to face a member named Dave. Always ill-tempered and confrontational, by now Dave had liberally appreciated the *gratis* wine placed on the tables and his drunken-ness was aggravated by an empty stomach.

"Whatthehellisgoingon?" Dave yelled. "Where's OUR food?"

Curt stood eye-to-eye with Dave, explaining quietly to him, hoping to de-escalate his agitation.

"Well, YOU got to eat, you bastard. Now deliver OUR food."

Seeing that it was pointless to repeat, and unable to think of anything more to say, Curt turned away.

Furious, Dave whirled Curt around, his fists clenched, and his face curled into a snarl. "Let's settle this outside!" His voice was sharp-edged.

Curt faced him. And gulped.

Muscular and compact, Dave could easily have killed Curt in a fistfight.

Then, past-Commodore Dick Hopper rose like a volcano from his nearby chair. "You'll have to get by me before you can start on him," he firmly stated, his eyes never leaving Dave's. None of us had ever seen this aspect of Hopper before.

Dave slowly backed away from the towering former base commander.

Now, if there's one thing I can't stand, it's to be an idle observer in a crisis when action must be taken. My brain had been racing and I had been fidgeting for over an hour since the big bang. *What could I do? How could I help?*

It was now around 8:30 and the rest of the membership must simply be *starving!* The caterer still hadn't returned.

I disengaged from those around me and went, unnoticed, to the cloak room. I slipped on my unbuttoned coat and pushed open the front door. The southeast storm wind carved me in my flimsy dress like a knife as I ran to the car. Kluey rose in greeting, thumping her tail against the windows from the flattened rear seats where she had been resting.

"Hi, Baby," I grinned grimly. "No, this isn't another potty break. You and I are going to beat feet to Safeway to get some food for the desperate masses."

Before I left home, I had put my driver's license, car keys and lipstick in my coat pocket, not needing cash or a purse. Now, as I raced toward Safeway, I had to make a plan to pay for the groceries for which I was going to beg.

At 8:45 the store was nearly empty and I was able to find the manager right away. He recognized me as being a regular customer but had never before seen me in formal evening clothes. It was obvious from my appearance that I was telling the truth when I blurted: "The stove at the yacht club blew up and we have hungry people there who are getting ornery." I pulled a diamond ring off my finger and handed it to him. "Will you take this as collateral and let me fill a shopping cart as fast as I can to the tune of about $100?"

He pressed the ring back into my hand. "I know you're good for it. Take a cart and get going."

"I'll be back to pay you by tomorrow morning," I said to him over my shoulder as I goosed the cart down the first aisle.

What can I get that has some class and doesn't need to be cooked? I thought as I screamed up and down the aisles.

Crackers, cheese, liver pate, shrimp, shrimp cocktail sauce…

I raced to the checkout counter, got a copy of the bill, wrote down my name and address, nodded my thanks to the manager and carried several bags out to the car.

Kluey could be trusted not to eat the groceries in the car, thank goodness. We arrived back at the clubhouse about 9:15.

I temporarily parked in the driveway as close as I could to the south side of building. My plan was to rap on the kitchen window and once it was opened, to pass the grocery bags inside through it. That way I could avoid making The Grand Entrance through a door that led directly from outside into the ballroom, followed immediately by another door that led from the ballroom into the kitchen. If I handed the groceries through the window, no one in the ballroom would have to see me or know about my delivery. After I re-parked the car, I could re-enter by the front door, hang up my coat and help the kitchen staff with what I had brought before I once again took my place in the ballroom.

I raised the tailgate and left it open. It didn't matter that the dog jumped out because it would take me a couple trips to haul the grocery bags to the kitchen window. Then I could put her back in the car.

Buggers! The window was completed fogged over from the heat and humidity inside and the cold outside. No one could see me as I knocked on it repeatedly. Finally, someone nudged it open. I told him to open it wide so that I could hand him the bags. He nodded *OK*.

But instead of opening the *window*, he opened the very kitchen side door that I had wanted to avoid, and then he opened the ballroom door to the outside. When that door, with its overhead floodlight glaring, was opened, I was spotlighted outside while gusts of icy wind instantly got everyone's attention. While I stood helplessly holding the groceries, my 80 lb. mostly-white marshmallow dog pranced inside and recognized the very first people she met, our friends Donna and Bob Cole.

"KLUEY! HOW ARE YOU, GIRL?"

Kluey was quite comfortable inside the clubhouse, having spent a considerable amount of time with us there when it was being built. My job during the building process was to sweep up all the little messes made by the various workmen — both volunteers and professionals — who always disregarded the fact that somebody had to clean up after them. I often had Kluey with me.

She couldn't have been more delighted to be there, wagging and cuddling with the Coles, her long white shedding hair wafting over the dark suits and dresses as she busily greeted friends. I couldn't grab her with my arms full of grocery bags, so she managed to find a few other people as well before I shrieked for her to obediently "Come" to me.

We backed out the door.

I was horrified. I was sure The Wives were horrified. Curt must *certainly* be horrified. The only ones who weren't might have been Kluey and the Coles.

I took a short walk for her to pee and for me to catch my breath, then re-parked the car and re-entered the front door. I hung up my coat and ducked into the kitchen before anyone in the ballroom could see me.

And there I intended to stay for the rest of the night.

If not the rest of my life.

In self-appointed charge of the kitchen was Curt's next-in-command, the Vice-Commodore. However, one of the ongoing bones-of-contention with the Old Guard of the yacht club was that this Vice-Commodore was a woman.

A woman!

What was the last bastion of Manhood coming to?

And this woman was not only a woman, but a Brit, and a retired minor league British actress with a very indulgent and permissive American husband.

Her name was Frieda.

Frieda bustled in without asking and just took things over. After all, she had already done The Unthinkable.

When the club used to meet for its monthly potlucks at the rented Odd Fellows Hall, it was an expected part of tradition that the Commodore's wife personally and single-handedly wash all the dishes following the meal.

Others dried, but SHE washed.

Thus, such lovely ladies as Dottie Shelley and Molly Hopper perspired for at least an hour over a sink load of hot water and messy dishes.

Frieda set about to end that tradition with the advent of the new clubhouse: someone other than the Commodore's wife would do that ugly job.

Together with other helpers, Frieda and I began to unpack my groceries and sort out what we could use when the kitchen door burst open again.

At last, the caterer reappeared, complete with his staff and their prepared food.

They totally disregarded my efforts and set about serving at once.

Things were again under control. I was excused.

But I wasn't about to retake my place in the ballroom. I was exhausted and embarrassed. And safe...in the kitchen.

And there I stayed until I was sure everyone had eaten.

When the speeches began, Frieda went out to take her place in the ballroom while Curt thanked the outgoing officers and presented the proper burgees to those incoming.

Frieda then stuck her head back inside the kitchen door and ordered me to come out.

I refused.

"But, Barb, you've *got* to come out. You're to be presented an award."

Dear God! Just what I need! I thought.

I still hesitated, so she came over to take me by the arm and prod me onto the ballroom stage. There she pinned a small golden anchor onto my top in recognition of my special services to the club, which, in my opinion, consisted mostly of sweeping up construction dust.

The music, the dancing, the remainder of the evening ran on as a muddled, but merciful, blur.

When everyone finally left and Curt was locking the doors, he and I looked at each other, laughing weakly, held hands and walked to the car.

Audrey Mackaman

Audrey Mackaman grew up in Des Moines, Iowa, reading fantasy novels and hoping someday to write her own. Now she lives on Whidbey Island in Washington, where she helps aspiring authors with their books while writing her own. Her middle grade series, Cavall in Camelot, is available through HarperCollins.

The Midnight Ferry

"See the Northwest by bike, they said. It'll be fun, they said."

"Would you stop complaining for *one minute*?"

"And you...you're the one who said we should take the *scenic route*. The *fifty-mile* scenic route."

"*Stop complaining*," Amelia hissed through clenched teeth. "Yeah, okay, it took longer than I thought." Not that she would change a thing. She'd been saving money all year for this trip, and she was going to enjoy every scenic vista, every winding bike trail and cliff-top overlook the Pacific Northwest had to offer. After this, it was back to Wisconsin for her final semester. And after that, real life. Cold and harsh and so obscured in darkness she could hardly see anything at all.

So, no, she wasn't going to let Dylan ruin this for her.

"It's dark, Melia," he huffed. He wasn't in the best shape, but he'd agreed—they'd *both* agreed—to do this by bike. "Does the ferry even run this late?"

They had reached the outskirts of town. A sign up ahead offered enough light to illuminate the words "Welcome to Port Townsend." Amelia dismounted her bike, reached into her backpack, and unfolded the ferry schedule under one of the sign's lamps. "The last one is at 8:30."

"And what time is it now?"

Amelia checked her watch. "9:43."

"Great!" Dylan's bike clattered as he let is fall over. "That's just great. What now?"

"Calm down. It's not that big of a deal. We can find a place in town."

Dylan grumbled something darkly under his breath but picked up his bike. At least they were on paved road again, and the ride into town was smooth. It was early October. The weather was nice, a bit chilled, but it tempered the crowds she'd been told descended here in the summer. As it was, they met only one or two cars, their headlights blinding as they turned a curve. Otherwise, it was as dark as the deserted country roads of Wisconsin.

There were more lights as they rolled into town. The first structure to greet them was the ferry terminal, with its expanse of paved concrete leading out to the dock. Farther out, docked between two massive pylons, the ferry waited like a great, patient beast.

"I thought you said the last ferry was at 8:30," Dylan called.

"That's what the schedule says. They probably just dock it here for the night."

"Then why are all the lights on?"

Amelia couldn't say. It did look like all the operating lights were on. The car lanes were empty, though.

Dylan's brakes squealed as he slowed and pulled over. "Melia, there are people onboard."

Amelia stopped too. If she looked closer, she could see the people Dylan was talking about, milling about on the deck. They didn't look like janitors or anything like that. And besides, there were more people inside, much more than would be needed for custodial staff.

"Well…huh." She cocked her head. "I guess the schedule could be wrong. Let's take a look."

They walked their bikes to the kiosk. The light was on inside and the window was open, though there was nobody manning the desk.

Amelia leaned her head in. "Hello?" she called.

"Hey, man," a voice called to them from across the lot, "you don't gotta mess with all that." They turned to see a man waving to them from the loading ramp. With his bell-bottom pants and flared-collar shirt, he looked like he was on his way to a costume party. An impression that was not dispelled when they came closer and Amelia could make out the paisley print of the shirt and the man's perm-curled hair. He grinned and continued waving them forward. "The midnight ferry's always free."

"I didn't know there was a midnight ferry," Amelia said as she wheeled her bike over the lip of the loading ramp. There was an odd assortment of cars in the holding deck. Amelia's father collected and repaired antique cars, so she could pick them out and name them all: a '77 Thunderbird, a pink '62 Cadillac, a freakin' Model A Ford… "Does the ferry always run this late?"

"Oh yeah," the man said. "I take it all the time. Name's Ted, by the way." He held out a hand.

"Amelia," she said. He had one of those too tight handshakes, which she returned. Dylan winced when it was his turn.

"You two from out of town?"

"Wisconsin."

"Ah, out seeing the Pacific Northwest? Romantic getaway, that sort of thing?"

"Oh, no," Dylan sputtered. "It's not like—we're not—"

"My *girl*friend couldn't make it," Amelia explained, putting emphasis on the word, an almost provocation. *Have a problem with that?* "She's back in Wisconsin."

Ted blinked, as if processing the implication, before grinning. "Right on," he said with a bobbing nod. "Love is love, man." He turned on his heels and motioned for them to follow. "Come on. I'll give you Wisconsinites a lesson on the sound."

Dylan gave her a questioning look. She shrugged. It couldn't hurt. He seemed friendly enough.

They followed him up the stairs to the main cabin, bouncing their bikes over every step. The other ferries they'd ridden had had special bike ramps for this sort of thing, but this ferry—the name on the faded headboard read *Illahee*—seemed a bit...shabbier than the others. Not as up to date. Dylan seemed to have noticed the same thing. "Could use a new coat of paint," he said, running his hand along the flaking handrail.

"Ah, give the old girl a break," Ted called over his shoulder. "She's been ferrying folks here and there for over eighty years." He patted the iron hull affectionately—was that a mood ring on his finger? "Started her life in San Francisco Bay, just like me. Guess I've always thought we were kindred spirits."

They reached the passenger deck.

"Costume party?" Dylan said, managing to sound as sardonic as possible.

All up and down the long hall were the people

they'd seen from the streets, dressed in an array of period costumes. Some of them, at least. Amelia spotted more hippies like their friend, Ted—fringes, tassels, bell-bottoms, flowing skirts and sleeves, tie-dye—but also swing dresses and greaser jackets from the '50s, zoot suits from the '40s, bobbed haircuts and cloche hats from the '30s... Newer stuff too, like '80s spandex and '90s denim.

It might have been a costume party, except that nobody was mingling like it was a party. Conversation never rose above a gentle din, like what you'd hear in a restaurant. Or on an airplane or bus, when strangers were forced together for a period of time while the vessel shuttled them from Point A to Point B. No music. No food.

Who were all these people?

"Everyone's just doin' their own thing," Ted said, redirecting Amelia's attention. "Say, it's a nice night. Want to hang out on the deck?"

"I...sure?" Again, they followed behind him, as if being pulled along on a line.

The deck lighting was harsh and drowned out the view of the water below, but Amelia could still hear the lapping of waves in the dark. Off in the distance, lights shimmered on the tide line from the little houses up on Whidbey's bluffs that rose up along the west side of the island. The *Illahee*'s deck wrapped all around the cabin, allowing for a potential 360-degree view of the sound if you were inclined to do some walking. It seemed Ted was. He continued leading them.

"How long you here for?" Ted asked as they walked.

"Two weeks," Amelia said. "Mid-semester break."

Two weeks. Not enough time to see every island in the San Juans. She'd had to prioritize, make a list, cut it down, plan it out. Whidbey for sure. Great biking, she'd heard. Trails that went for miles and miles up and down the island—it was the largest of the San Juans, after all, if not *technically* a San Juan Island itself.

"S'posed to be pretty over there," Ted said, as if reading her thoughts. "Big old rainforests, wide open pastures, lots of great ocean views."

"You've never been?" Dylan asked in surprise.

Ted shrugged. "Ridden the ferry enough, sure. Going back and forth, back and forth, but never..." He leaned against the railing and stared out at the darkness. "It never comes on anymore, but they have this little lighthouse up on the high bluff there. You can see it from the docks."

Amelia and Dylan looked at each other.

"Would you...like to come with us when we get off?" Amelia asked. "We were planning on hiking at Ebey's Landing...where the lighthouse is."

Ted was silent, his thoughts far away from them.

Overhead, a horn blasted, and the ferry jolted as it began to move.

"Thanks, man," Ted said, turning away from the railing. "I appreciate the offer, but it's not really what I do." He sat himself down on one of the long benches under the cabin awning. He reached into his pants pocket and pulled out a pack of cigarettes. "The *Illahee* almost never made it up here. From San Francisco Bay, I mean. When they were bringing the old ships up. She hit a storm. All passengers had to be evacuated. She almost never saw land again."

"Yeah?" Amelia couldn't tell if Dylan was genuinely interested or simply placating their guide. "You know a lot about the ferries around here?"

"I know a lot about *Illahee*." He tapped a cigarette out of the pack and produced a small, silver lighter. Then lit up like it was nothing. "She was built in 1927. Ten years later, the Golden Gate Bridge went up and she was made obsolete. The Puget Sound Navigation Company still had use for her and her sisters, so they brought her up here, put her on the Seattle-Bremerton run. She's done all the crossings in the sound at one time or another, though."

The end of his cigarette glowed orange in the dark, and as he exhaled, a cloud of smoke wafted over them. Amelia held her nose against it, but Dylan coughed and tried to wave it away with his hand. "Those things can kill you, you know," he said.

Ted held the cigarette between his index and middle fingers, contemplating it.

At last he said, "Why do ghosts wear clothes?"

"What?" The change in topic was so sudden, Amelia wasn't sure she'd heard properly.

"Ghosts," Ted repeated, flicking the ash from his cigarette. "In all the stories you hear, they're always wearing clothes. Like the ladies in the white gowns and the soldiers in their Civil War uniforms and whatever. Why is that?"

Perhaps there was more than tobacco in what he was smoking?

"Like," he continued when neither of them

responded, "ghosts are supposed to be the spirits of people who've died, right? So, do their clothes have spirits too? Do you only get to take one change of clothes with you to the afterlife, and that's whatever you were wearing when you died?" He took another drag. "Just seems weird to me."

"I…guess I never thought about it," Dylan said.

"Know what I think?" Ted leaned forward, gesturing to the two of them with his cigarette. "I think ghosts aren't really spirits. I think they're kind of like…memories."

A strong gust blew in from the water, raising the hair on the back of Amelia's neck. She pulled her windbreaker closer.

"Images," Ted went on, "like photonegatives. You've got something that leaves such a strong impression—like what a person was wearing when they died, their last actions, what have you—and it *burns* an image into that place." He dropped his cigarette and stamped it out with his shoe. The smell of smoke lingered on the air. "Places have memories, you know. You can't deny that."

"I suppose not." Amelia watched the wind pick up the ashes.

"The past is an anchor. It never moves." Ted shook his head. "Ghosts, the past…the *future* is where it's at, man. Memories that haven't been *made* yet."

He looked like he was going to reach for another cigarette, but was interrupted by another loud blast of the horn from above. "Attention all passengers," a man's voice called over a tinny PA system, "we are now reaching our destination. Please return to your vehicles. Foot passengers assemble at the disembarkation area at the bow."

Amelia looked to Dylan, who had gone almost completely white. "We better get going," she said, snapping him out of his daydream. "Are you sure you don't want to get off with us?"

Ted waved her off. "Enjoy the lighthouse for me," he said. "Hope you have a good time." As they headed back into the cabin, he called out to them, "Oh, and good luck on your next semester. Don't fear the future, man!"

They were the only ones in the loading dock, either on foot or by car. As Amelia went to get her bike, she saw a lone ferry worker manning the rope. He looked washed out and gray, even in his neon-colored vest, but nodded to her. "Smooth ride tonight," he said.

Amelia nodded and used the heel of her shoe to kick back her kickstand. She and Dylan walked their bikes to the bow. The shape of the pylons greeted them. The entire ship shook as it slowed and edged towards the dock. Amelia nearly fell over, but the ferry worker remained steadfast. *Sea legs*, Amelia thought, and wondered how many times the man had ridden this ferry back and forth, back and forth over the years.

"You folks enjoy your stay on Whidbey," he said as he unclipped the rope and stepped back to allow them to exit.

They both nodded.

The parking lot on this side of the ferry route was smaller, more contained. The overhead stadium lights cast a halo of fluorescent white over everything. Off to the left, the bluff with the lighthouse rose up over them, though there was no making anything out in the darkness. It probably wouldn't be a good idea to ride up there this time of night, but there was a camping area not far from the parking lot, along the beach that followed along the bluff. She could see the lights from the RV's parked there and, when the wind shifted, could smell the smoke from a bonfire.

Dylan was fidgety, and as soon as they reached the first lane of the parking lot, he mounted up on his bike.

"Woah, what's the rush?" Amelia laughed.

"I don't know. There's just…something weird about that Ted guy. About all of them." He frowned at her, as if asking why she wasn't on her bike yet. "Didn't you feel it?"

Amelia shrugged. "Nothing weirder than what you'd see on campus on a Saturday night."

"No, I mean…" He lifted out the armpits of his biking shirt. "Smell my shirt."

"What?" Amelia balked. "I'm not smelling your pit stink."

"Then smell your own shirt."

With a sigh, she turned her head and buried her nose into her shoulder. The sleek material of her athletic wear was stiff from a day's worth of dried sweat, but nothing they hadn't been dealing with on a daily basis from this trip. "What am I smelling for?"

"You smell any smoke?"

"Smoke?" She sniffed again. "No."

"You don't smell Ted's cigarettes?"

She paused. "No," she answered slowly,

confused now. He'd been blowing smoke straight at them, but she couldn't detect a trace of it on her clothes. She pulled her ponytail over her shoulder and smelled that too, but again, no smoke. "Huh, that's really..."

"Weird, right?" Dylan finished.

Amelia glanced over her shoulder, as if another look at the ferry would give her insight into this weirdness. It didn't. There was no ferry to see. The *Illahee* was gone, as if vanished into thin air.

"What...?" She turned around to make sure she wasn't seeing things—or *not* seeing things, as the case may be. But no, the pylons stood empty, and the stadium lights from the parking lot illuminated the empty spot where the boat had been only a minute ago. Her head swiveled back to Dylan to see if she was imagining things. By the roundness of his eyes, she wasn't. "I'm not going crazy, am I?" she asked, just in case.

He put one foot up on the bike's peddles. "Can we go now?"

Jan Wright

Jan moved to Whidbey Island in 2007. Besides writing, in her retirement years she's had the good fortune to fly a helicopter, to go rafting in the Grand Canyon, to swim with whale sharks, and to perform in a musical comedy. As a world traveler, she has photographed wild animals on safari in Africa, hiked Machu Picchu, and learned to speak enough Creole to communicate with children while she helped to build a church and school in Haiti. Always a teacher at heart, she has shared her adventures through writing, annotated photobooks, and group presentations. She is the author of Dear Mrs. Wright, A Teacher's Memoir Inspired by Students' Letters.

Surrogate

A blanket of dark storm clouds smothered the expansive view of Admiralty Inlet and the Straits of Juan de Fuca. February winds picked up, moaning and rattling the windows. In my nightgown and robe, I sat alone in the living room chair, feet up on the hassock, having a hard time concentrating on the TV program. Splatters of raindrops drew my eyes to the viewless picture window while my mind wandered through a wasteland of loss.

My friend, Barry, had died on Christmas Day. He no longer drove me to choir practice on Wednesday nights. He would never again take me out for the occasional dinner. How could he be gone? How could he be erased from my life so suddenly? Just like my dear husband. Had it really been seven whole years since Paul's death? Intensified by the wild weather, loneliness seeped into my being. Storm-isolated on Whidbey Island, I didn't want to just sit there, but what else could I do? I sank deeper into dismal thoughts and depression.

Then, on quiet paws, Patches appeared and settled on the floor beside my chair. I looked down into his unblinking, yellow eyes. The cat held my gaze.

"You can come up," I said aloud to him, patting my lap.

He continued to stare.

"You never follow commands, do you?"

On his own time, he bounded up into my lap. Standing with his front paws on my chest, he nuzzled my cheek. I stroked his soft fur, feeling the weight of his fourteen-pound body drilled into my thighs and chest through his feet.

His muscles relaxed, and he slid down into the crook of my arm. I held onto him like a baby. I ran my free hand around his ears, under his chin, over the top of his head. Again. Again. Again. He purred, responding to my touch. I watched his eyes flutter and then close.

"Are you here to remind me I am not completely alone?" I wondered.

He shifted his position once more and curled into my lap. Finding the upturned palm of my hand, he laid his head in it. I continued to pet his soft body with the other hand. He pulled his paws up to his face and tucked his cute little head between them. His purring resonated through my body. I gazed at the living ball of fur in my lap, so tender, so trusting. The room seemed to fade away, as if the sound had muted and the lights had dimmed. A warmth settled in my heart, banishing the cold storm of lonely thoughts.

Purring ceased and Patches began to snore. I found myself smiling at the sleeping cat.

"You sweet little boy, I'm so glad you came into my life," I whispered to him.

The Audition

Pam strummed her fingers on the steering wheel, waiting for the light to change. She could see the Whidbey Playhouse Theater just around the corner.

Thank goodness I found it! I knew it was on Midway, but I don't come to Oak Harbor often enough to remember exactly how to get here. There's so much traffic these days, especially in the summer with all the tourists.

The traffic light remained red.

That old church building must be nearly 100 years old. I wonder how they managed to turn it into such a thriving community theater.

She chuckled to herself.

It's just like me: still a lot of life left in the old girl.

The light turned green.

Pam turned the car into the parking area beside the theater, relieved to find the Star Studio tucked into the back of the lot. She parked her car, hurried across the pavement, and stepped through the open door to the studio with barely two minutes to spare.

The young lady at the desk smiled and asked her, "Are you here to audition?"

"Yes," she answered with what she hoped sounded like confidence.

"You need to fill out this form," the young lady said, holding out papers with one hand and a pen with the other. "Sit down somewhere. I don't have any clip boards right now."

The tiny entry room, a kind of lobby, was filled with young people sitting on chairs, standing by the edge of the door, and sitting on the floor. The space buzzed with people talking to each other.

"I'm sorry, what did you say?"

"I don't have any clip boards."

"Oh, that's OK. I can manage."

As crowded as the lobby seemed to be, Pam was surprised to see an empty wooden bench. Although narrow, it would do, so she sat. She placed her purse on the floor by her feet and set the papers on her thigh.

Hmmm, what do they want to know about me? I thought I filled out the basics online already.

Name. Address. *I think I'll print, make it easy to read. They're not teaching cursive handwriting in* *the schools any more.*

__Cell Number.__ I don't usually give that out. They might need to text me, if I get a part. OK. I'll do it just this time.

__Estimated Age.__ Estimated? Why estimate? I'm just going to write my age, 71. It's not often I need to write my age these days.

__If you're under 18, parent's name.__ That's definitely not me, but I guess it might apply to some of these young folks in here.

Should I erase that 71? Maybe this age thing doesn't apply to me. Maybe I should estimate. What would I write instead? My hair is not even gray yet. Maybe I should just let them guess. Nope. I am 71, so that's what I'll stick with.

__Emergency contact.__ I'm a widow; that one still bothers me. Why would they need this information anyway? What's dangerous about being in a little local musical? I guess they need to be concerned about liability. I'll just put my neighbor's name here. No need to notify my son in California.

"It's time," the Director said in an authoritative tone of voice as he entered the lobby from the open doorway beside her. "Come into the next room. You can fill out those papers later. We need to get started."

Pam picked up her purse and carried the pen and papers around the corner, through the doorway. She paused to look around. The large room was already filled with people seated around the perimeter. Floor-to-ceiling mirrors covered one entire wall. The space was unexpectedly clean and bright.

This is a great space for dancing! It looks so

different from the theater itself, that old church building. They must be doing all right to have this beautiful new practice space.

She saw an open bench at the far corner, next to a piano. At that end of the room, four people sat behind tables smiling at the assembled group.

Pam walked across the room and took a seat as the Director began to talk to the group about "The Addams Family Musical." He introduced the people behind the tables as the assistant director, the music director, the piano player, and one of the dance choreographers. Of course, their names immediately evaporated from her memory. Trying to keep her focus on his words, she attempted to complete the paper form in front of her.

Performances you've been in and roles you've played. *Oh gosh, when was the last time I did anything like this? Should I include the role of Innkeeper in the Christmas skit last year. No, I don't think so. I'll just skip this section for now.*

Having difficulty concentrating, she realized the young lady from the lobby stood beside her trying to hand her a clipboard.

"Oh, thank you," Pam said, as she began to struggle to set the papers under the clip.

What is this second paper? Oh, it's a rehearsal schedule. Good. I'll need that, I hope. At least I don't have to write anything on that page.

The Director continued talking about the plot of the musical and his vision for humor.

Pam scanned the room, but did not see anyone she knew.

"Let's begin the group dance auditions. Be sure

to add the character traits you've worked on as you dance. Remember, we want you to stand out," he encouraged.

But I haven't finished this paper! OK, OK, I need to think about the dancing. Let's see, the Director said to add character traits? How do I portray the part of an ancestor? Dead? No, I don't think so. I think he's talking to those who are auditioning for one of the main parts. I just want to be in the ensemble, to dance in the background. I think I'll just be myself and "act" the way the music makes me feel.

The dance leader walked to the middle of the room. The statuesque beauty smiled, eyes sparkling as she spoke, "…All right, everyone up and face the mirrors."

Did I miss her name? She must have been introduced. I'll just set this clipboard down and pay better attention.

Pam stood up. While others scrambled to be in the back, she determinedly walked to the front row, and stood beside the dance leader. Looking in the mirror, she pulled on the hem of her blouse in a vain attempt to minimize the annoying bulging rolls of her tummy. Then she straightened up her posture.

That's better. Not quite as slim as I used to be, but not looking too bad these days either. At least my hair looks good today. Just smile; you'll do fine.

"Oh, this is a big group. Let's make three lines then," said the leader.

Pam watched the dancers in the mirror as she shifted forward, remaining steadfast to her front and center position.

Am I being too bold? No. I'm short. I need to see what's going on. This is an audition. It's no time to be shy. He did say to stand out, so here I am.

The dance leader began. "We will go through all the steps once together, and then I will sit down and watch you. We start with a line dance. Step to the right, behind, kick. All right, everyone, do that with me. Step right, behind, kick."

Pam moved with the group to the right.

"Good. Now to the left. Step left, behind, kick."

Oh, this is easy. It's exactly like the practice video.

The instruction continued and the group danced on until the entire set was complete.

"Now we will break up into three smaller groups, and I will watch you perform," said the dance leader. The dancers stood waiting, shifting uncomfortably from one foot to the other while the dance leader figured out what to do next.

"Let's see, how many are there?"

Pam quickly figured out the total. Several people began to talk at once.

Should I just blurt out the number? No, I've got to remember to be patient. This is theater. It's going to take time for the creative process.

Finally, the dance leader pointed to each dancer, slowly counting them.

"1, 2, 3, 4 . . ."

Oh, good grief, can this go any slower? I just want to get this over with.

". . . 11, 12, 13. I got thirteen. Is that right? OK. Go ahead and sit down."

Pam sat. She usually volunteered to go first for

most things, but the unfinished form nagged at her, so she hesitated while the first five dancers jumped up and took their place on the floor.

OK. I can go next, after I finish this page.

She went back to the blank section and searched her brain for dance experiences.

At college I was best dancer and choreographer of the year, 1969. Hmmm, maybe that was a bit too long ago. I'm just going to skip this part about experience. I'll think about it later.

She took a good look around the room, as the dancers maneuvered to organize the Bunny Hop part of the dance.

Holy cow! I must be at least 50 years older than anyone else doing this dance audition. How did that happen? Maybe there were some older folks at yesterday's audition.

She kept working on the papers, filling in phone numbers and email addresses. The leader called for the second group of dancers. Four more got up before Pam realized what was happening.

Gee, there's a back side to this page too. I just want to watch the dancers and see what I'm up against. I'll just hurry up and finish.

She completed the form just as the second group ended their audition.

"All right, who's next?" asked the dance leader, looking to her right. "Wait, there's only three?"

"I'm over here," Pam shouted, waving her hand to get attention.

The leader turned toward her, "Oh, there you are."

Pam got up, stood in the front row of the little

audition group, and looked at herself in the mirror and smiled. All the eyes in the room were on her and the three other dancers.

I know this dance. The heck with everyone watching me! I'm just going to enjoy myself.

She took a deep breath and squared her shoulders.

"You're Pam Evans, right?"

Pam nodded.

She knows my name? I guess at my age, I do stand out a bit.

"I've heard a lot about you," said the dance leader.

"Uh oh," said Pam with a grin, eyes rolling.

Diane, my exercise teacher, must have told her about me. Good thing Diane told me about this audition. It's about time I did something like this. I wonder what she said about me....

The leader continued to write the names of the other dancers until she completed the list.

"OK, start the music."

"Wait," interrupted Pam. "Can we organize the Bunny Hop line first?"

"Oh, yes, of course. Let's see. Pam, why don't you lead the line? The rest of you fall in place behind her.   The tallest needs to be in the back."

They lined up with Pam in front, and then they returned to the starting positions.

The music began.

I can do this. I can do this. Hop like a bunny in the front of the line.   Here comes the twist. Just let loose and, wahoo, dance! Back to the line dance. Right, behind, kick.

She glanced up at the mirrors.

Yikes! We're not in unison. The group looks awful! Is it me? Am I off with timing? Just ignore the others and concentrate on the music. Stop thinking so much. Just dance!

Last step, rigor mortis. Leg up, hold my balance, look dead....

The audience clapped. She walked back to her seat at the bench. A woman on the bench next to her gave her a high five and a big grin.

Oh, that was unexpected! Aaaaa, it wasn't my best, but what's done is done.

"Thanks everyone. We will start the singing auditions right away," announced the Director. "Pam Evans is first. The rest of you, stick around, and we'll call you in order after that. All right. Everyone out, except Pam. We'll keep the door closed during these private auditions."

She followed the Director through the door and handed her paperwork on the clipboard to the lady in the lobby while the room emptied, then walked back and stood near the piano. Only the five judges remained.

Yikes, this is the part I've been dreading, singing. Solo. In front of these folks who will decide my fate. I'm so glad I signed up early and got the first time slot. There's nothing more I can do to prepare, so I'm just going to sing out with confidence, as if I know what I'm doing.

She faced the panel. The lady with the red hair and a warm smile said, "I'm Marti. I am the music director. I remember meeting you at the preview night. You said you could dance, but you were nervous about singing a solo. Right?"

"Yes, that's right. I do sing in a choir, but solo singing is not my thing."

Oh, she's the one Diane introduced me to that night. Wow! She's got a good memory. I didn't realize she was going to decide my audition fate. I'm surprised she remembered me. Oh, I do hope I made a good impression.

"I want to learn your range first. You will sing scales with the piano."

"Oh, I get to sing with the piano? Cool!"

"The word you will sing is la."

Did I hear her right?

"La?"

"Yes, la."

Pam nearly laughed out loud. "Well, that's easy. La."

The pianist began to play. Pam sang the familiar scales easily, just as she did with her church choir, reaching a higher and higher pitch until she began to feel uncomfortable and scrunched up her face and quit.

"You could keep going. You were doing fine," encouraged Marti.

"I like singing lower. I'm an alto," said Pam.

"OK, then let's try singing to the low end. Sing: 'Down to the bottom of the boat.'"

"Down to the bottom of the boat. Down to the bottom of the boat," sang Pam.

This is silly ...and easy. I am enunciating perfectly. It's comfortable for my voice. I wonder what the Director and Assistant Director are doing? Don't look at them, just stay focused on the music.

Pam continued, "Down to the bottom of the boat. Down to the bottom of the boat. Down to the bottom of the boat."

"OK, good. We'll stop there. Now I want you to sing 'Row, Row, Row Your Boat.' I will sing with you at first and then you keep going and I will come in, a phrase after you. I also want to see how loud you can sing."

Is she kidding? Can I sing a round of "Row, Row, Row Your Boat"? I've taught this to many of my students. I can blast this one out of the park!

In no time, this part of the singing audition was complete, and it was finally time to sing the song that made her most nervous, "When You're an Addams."

"Did you practice the alto line for this one?"

"Yes."

I did practice, but I'm still not sure I've got it right. Stop being nervous! My throat will tighten up, and I'll sound terrible.

"Would you like me to sing with you?" said the kindly lady.

"Fantastic! Yes!"

What a relief! I'm home free. I know I can sing with her. It's so much easier than singing alone against that awful recording.

They sang together. The notes Marti sang were a little different than the ones Pam had practiced, but easy to follow, so she did. At the end, Pam confidently slid down the notes and jumped up to the final high note. Marti sang the low note.

Marti said to the pianist, "She's the first one who did that!"

"Was it wrong?" Pam asked.

"No, not at all. It was just right. Can you sing the low note while I sing the high note?"

"Sure."

"You do what Addams do or die," they sang together, ending at opposite octaves.

"Great. You did just fine. Thank you, Pam."

"Thank you. This was fun!"

The Director spoke up, "When you go out, tell them to get the next person up for audition. We will let them know when we are ready."

"Ok. Thanks!"

She walked out with a spring in her step.

I'm done. There's nothing more I can do to make my audition any better.

She studied the theater building as she got into her car. The tall windows were boarded up. A coat of beige paint with blue trim took away some of the former-church look. A bright blue canopy marked the current entrance, standing over stairs descending into a basement level set of double doors. The large street-side front doors were apparently unused in this theater incarnation of the building.

I hope I'll get to work on the stage inside that theater. They did a lot of renovation on the old building. Maybe they'll take a chance on me, too.

She went grocery shopping. She did laundry. She answered emails. She made dinner. All the while, she analyzed and reanalyzed her audition performance until she began to slip into acceptance that she might not make it and might not hear from the directors.

At 6:30 PM her cell phone rang. She picked it up and stared at the number on the screen.

Should I answer? I don't know this number. There's no name. Maybe it's about my audition. Guess I'd better take a chance.

"Hello?"

"Hello. Is this Pam Evans?"

"Yes."

"This is Bart Shoenig. I'm the Assistant Director for the Addams Family Musical. We'd like to offer you a part as an ancestor."

"Wahoo!" she yelled.

"I'll take that as a 'Yes' then?"

"Yes, indeed!"

"Congratulations. Our first meeting is this Thursday at 6:30."

"I'll be there!"

I did it! I did it! One more bucket list item to check off. I'm going to dance on the stage again. I'm going to be a dancing, singing ancestor.

An ancestor.... Hey, was that type-casting?

"WAHOOO!"

A Mighty Chunk of Land
March 27, 2013
Based on True Events

A shiver ran through the doublewide manufactured house, waking the elderly man in the dead of the night. Michael strained to hear undefined noises. He couldn't quite place the source. Distant crashing waves coupled with snapping and shuddering sounds didn't seem right. An edgy feeling of something out of order kept him alert.

Vibrations began again, stronger, louder this time. Michael picked up his cell phone and dialed one of his few trusted contacts, someone he thought might be awake and give him guidance, his landlady.

Preparing for the workday in distant Texas, she responded to him without hesitation, "Get out immediately. I'll call 911 for you. Just go. NOW!"

Michael pulled on his sweatpants and hurried out of his house in the darkness, locking the door out of habit. He drove his truck forward until he heard . . . and felt . . . a loud, concussive *wuff*. In the beams of his headlights, the road ahead dropped out of sight. He threw his truck into reverse and stepped on the gas, watching a gigantic avalanche of warped earth uplift and transport his home in front of him. The house slid on its steel girders with the shifting and cracking ground. As the land moved, it pulled electric power poles down like dominoes, hurling them along with crashing trees. A massive relocation of terrain tore apart and destroyed the roadway, the only exit for vehicles. The old man, the sole observer, sat alone in his truck, trapped at the end of the road.

When the initial movement stopped, the toe of the slide protruded over 250 feet from the original line of shore bulkheads into the cold waters of Admiralty Inlet. The beach surface was uplifted twenty to thirty feet high. The old man's house sat on the jumbled mass of displaced land, perched precariously above the beach.

At the end of the road, Michael's neighbors awoke to the sound of a loud, house-shaking, *thunk*. Roused from sleep, Susan tried to turn on the light. Nothing. She lit a bedside candle and glanced at the face of the clock. It read 3:20 a.m.

Susan padded through the darkened house and peered through the front windows at what looked like headlights on the street in front of their house. She slipped on her shoes and threw on a warm coat to go outside, where she discovered the dazed old man standing beside his truck. "Are you okay?" she asked.

"A tremendous landslide took my house and the road with it." He paused and nearly whispered, "There's no way out."

"Oh my...that must have been the noises we heard," she murmured.

She took a deep breath and said, "We need to wait for daylight when we can see better. If the road is really gone, we'll need help. Electric power out, but we do have a woodstove. Why don't you come inside with my mother and me where it's warm?"

In the modest beach cottage, the trio heated water for coffee over a woodstove and waited together for daylight and rescue.

On the bluff 200 feet above Michael's house, a sonic boom-like sound and the agitation of his dog woke Eric. The young man shoved his feet into slippers. With a dimming flashlight in his hand, Eric and his dog ventured out into the moonlit darkness across an expansive back yard. Unable to see much, he shook the flashlight. The light went out. "Come on, Chester, let's go in and get new batteries for this damn flashlight."

Eric and the dog returned to the house, changed batteries, and went back outside to look again. They stopped short. The spot where they had stood, only moments before, had vanished from sight. An enormous chunk of land and all the trees that rimmed the bluff were . . . gone.

One year before, Eric's stepmother had passed away after a lengthy and valiant fight against cancer; his dad had followed his beloved wife six months later. This house had been the family center. Eric led their dog, now his, back into the house, grabbed the whiskey bottle and a glass. He slumped into a living room chair.

A few minutes later, a few doors down from Eric, the phone rang at Simon's house.

"This is Bay Alarm System. Is this Simon Wagner?" said a female voice.

"Yes, it is," answered Simon.

"You're listed as an emergency contact for the Holland family. The alarm went off in their house. There was no response when we called. Could you check to see if they are all right and call us back to let us know?"

"Sure thing." Simon hung up the phone and slipped out of bed.

"What's going on?" asked his wife.

"I'm going over to check out the Hollands' house, Patricia. They're out of town again, but something has made the alarm go off."

"You be careful," she said.

"There's a full moon tonight. Should be easy to see, but I'll take the big flashlight."

Simon dressed, grabbed the flashlight, and headed out across the street just as the sheriff arrived. Together they circled the house, peering into the windows, and trying the door handles. They found nothing out of order. The Sheriff filled out a card to leave a notice of inspection for the owners, called the alarm company, and departed. Simon returned home.

After a trip to the bathroom, Simon headed back toward the bedroom. He glanced out the window and saw something unusual, a clear view of the Salish Sea and the twinkling lights of Port Townsend. The cedar tree was missing. Then he felt a vibration and heard a distant rumble.

At 4:10 a.m., Raymond awoke not quite sure what had disturbed the peace and silence of the night. A distant sound like shushing? A tremor of the land?

The splintering, fracturing of . . . trees? Awareness seeped into his mind, transforming a sense of unease into comprehension. He stood up and peered out the window into the ghostly lit night as the phone began to ring.

"Yeah," he said into the receiver.

"Raymond, did you feel that? Landslide. My cedar tree is gone," said Simon. "You know, as water commissioners, we've got to shut down the water main."

"I'll meet you out there as soon as I get Cindy and the cats safely out of the house," replied Raymond.

The full moon shown down on Raymond and Simon as they stood in the street near the water main shut off. Raymond turned his head, listening. "Do you hear any rushing water?"

"Not sure."

"Since it goes over and down the bluff, the line probably ruptured," said Raymond, thinking aloud.

"Well, we've trained for this. Let's do it," said Simon.

The two men wrestled with the oversized wrench until they maneuvered the valve into the closed position.

"Now let's go wake the folks on the bluff side of the street," said Raymond.

At 5:15 a.m., I awoke to the jarring ring of my phone. I listened as Raymond, speaking in a calm, controlled voice, relayed what had transpired. He finished by saying, "The fire department set up a command center at the top of the street leading down to the beach. I think you need to meet the Incident Commander. I'll come get you."

Fully awake now, I dressed in a hurry and bounded downstairs. I donned a warm jacket and wool hat just as the doorbell rang.

"You didn't drive?" I asked.

"Not sure how stable the bluff is," he said.

We held the incredulous thought for a moment.

"It's safer to walk," Raymond said with conviction. "Let's go."

In the moonlight, we walked down the hill, along the quiet street lined with houses perched on the hillside above the shoreline. We turned the corner at Seaview to head down toward the beach. Two firetrucks with emergency lights flashing blocked the path. In that single instant, the full impact of the emergency hit me.

Raymond walked me toward one of the young men standing in the street wearing full fireman gear. "Doris, meet Sam Brannon, the Incident Commander. Sam, this is Doris Pullman, the president of our neighborhood association I told you about. She's had a lot of emergency training."

As we shook hands, embarrassed by the presumption of my introduction, I explained, "I've been trained in Community Emergency Response Team and the National Incident Management System."

"NIMS? How did you get involved with that?" asked Sam with a smile.

"I was a Vice Principal in the San Francisco Bay Area and on the Safety Committee for my school district. With the Oakland Hills fire, we learned how important it is to have a universal communication and command system during an emergency. When the federal government created NIMS, we did the training," I replied, thinking I'd probably said more than necessary.

"I'm impressed. And, Island County hasn't done CERT training for several years."

"So, what can we do to help? What do you need?" I asked.

"Mostly, we're waiting for daylight, but my men have been checking all the houses on the bluff. We're evacuating the people who live along the west side of Fircrest Avenue. We need to set up a Disaster Relief Center in coordination with the Red Cross. Is there a place we can use for that?"

"Yes, we have a clubhouse, actually a former volunteer firehouse. It has a bathroom, a partial kitchen, and plenty of tables and chairs. I can have it opened up and ready for use. We also have an email system that I can use to let the neighborhood know what's going on and ask for any help you might need from us. We could provide coffee and a warm place to rest."

"That sounds great," Sam replied.

"What about the people who live below the bluff, at the end of the road?" I asked.

"We're waiting for daylight to assess the situation. It appears the road is impassable. We may need to bring in boats to rescue those folks if that's the case, since there's no other way to get to them."

"Oh, but there is a path down to the beach from the other end of Fircrest," said Raymond.

"We were not aware of that," replied the Incident Commander.

"It's narrow, overgrown, and not well known, but I've hiked down the path in the past to get to the beach. I can take some of your men down there," Raymond said.

"Good. We'll wait until the sun comes up," said Sam. "Meanwhile, I'll keep the rescue boats on standby."

I added, "I'll send someone up to the old firehouse to unlock it, put the lights on, and get the heater going."

Throughout the early morning hours, residents of the Ledgewood Beach area responded to my emails. They offered shelter in their homes and delivered stacks of bottled water, hot coffee, breakfast foods, and snacks to the newly designated Disaster Relief Center.

One of those who replied with a phone call was the elderly man's landlord, Sarah. "Thank God for your emails. I'm worried sick about Michael, my tenant down on Driftwood Way. He told me some neighbors took him into their house. His cell phone battery is running low, and they don't have any electricity down there. He's an independent loner, but I'm concerned because he's 82 years old and has some health issues."

"I know the firefighters are headed down to check on the folks below the bluff," I replied. "I'll see that he gets whatever help he needs. We've got power up here. Can you give me Michael's phone number?"

I dialed.

"Hello…" Michael answered in a tremulous voice.

"Michael, I'm Doris Pullman from Ledgewood. Sarah gave me your number."

I rushed on, "When the sun comes up, firemen will be coming down a path to get you. Are you all right? Do you need anything?"

"I'm okay, but I don't have anything with me except the keys to my truck, which is useless now. I need my medications. I can take the free bus into Freeland to get replacements when they get me out of here," he said.

"My goodness, you don't need to take a *bus!* We'll help you get what you need. I know a retired nurse in our neighborhood who will meet you when the firemen bring you to the top of the hill. She can make a few phone calls to get those prescriptions set up."

As the light of day doused the darkness of night, Raymond guided firefighters down the nearly hidden, overgrown pathway to reach the stranded neighbors below the bluff. Once they had made contact with each household, the first responders hiked back up the hill through the brush to retrieve equipment for clearing a rescue path. They spent the early morning hours hacking out the trail, making it wide enough to take a four-wheel drive utility vehicle down to the bottom.

By mid-morning I waited with a small cluster of neighbors and firefighters at the top of the hill. Laurie, a former nurse, stood beside me holding a blanket and a thermos of hot coffee.

A couple of vans with telescoping satellite dishes parked along the street nearby. A man shouldering a large camera followed a woman in a bright yellow jacket grasping a microphone as she worked her way through the group. Another TV news team in dark blue windbreakers trotted toward the growing crowd.

"Where were you when the landslide started?

"What did you notice first?

"Was your house affected by the slide?

"How many homes are at the bottom of the hill?"

The sound of an approaching motor on its ascent up the muddy slope seized their attention. All eyes turned to watch the UTV burst over the crest of the hill and into the sunlight, coming to a halt in front of the waiting group. More reporters ran toward the scene with cameras rolling.

The firefighters helped Michael climb out of the UTV. The shaken elderly man stood on wobbly legs, blinking at the crowd before him. I stepped forward and took one of his hands in mine.

"Hi, Michael. I'm Doris. I talked with you on the phone. This is Laurie, the nurse I told you about. She's going to take you to her house and get you settled. She'll help you get replacements for your medication. And, you can call your very concerned landlady."

More vehicles arrived on the street, and the sound of circling helicopters amplified the tension. Laurie and her husband led Michael to their waiting car and whisked him away to care for his needs. Left behind in his abandoned house were all his belongings: his eyeglasses, his clothes, his food, his tools, and his lifetime treasures.

Vast upwellings of clay had appeared on the beach. Land continued to shift in small increments for days. Adventurous residents captured the scenes on cell phones.

Reporters roamed the formerly quiet neighborhood in search of sensational interviews. Simon told them he watched a chunk of land as it "sliced off the bluff like a piece of bread." Raymond was quoted saying he now had "a million-dollar view with a five-dollar house."

Looky-loos cruised the streets, curious to see the great landslide. The sheriff finally ordered his men to barricade the entrance to the area. People as far away as Spain called to ask if friends and family were all right; they'd seen the massive slide on the TV news.

In the urgency of the days that followed, some forty neighbors worked at a frantic pace to help Eric pack up and move into storage a lifetime of accumulated family possessions from the bluff house. It would take years for him to sort through the stored items, surely prolonging the pain of bereavement.

Eventually, politicians came seeking publicity, and geologists came searching for answers. They estimated some 40,000 dump trucks of earth had moved. No loss of lives or physical injuries were reported. Six houses, two on the bluff and four below, were tagged by Island County as uninhabitable, condemned.

County officials forbade Michael to climb through the unstable chasms to reach his condemned house, but in the weeks and months that followed, devil-may-care punks made the treacherous trek up from the beach and stole his possessions. Then one night a fire burned the rest of the house to the ground as helpless neighbors and firefighters watched from a distance. The old man moved to California to be near his daughter.

The condemned bluff house that held cherished memories of three generations of a family dedicated in service to Ledgewood Beach and Whidbey Island now stands empty, only a few feet from demise over a still cleaving cliff. A once seventy-foot-wide lawn no longer grows to be mowed by a dedicated son, and the lovingly tended garden disappeared. The dog searched for his lost buried bones until he too passed away, leaving Eric alone, seeking a new place to live.

Below the bluff, electricity and broken water pipes were replaced. After a few years and a lawsuit, the county rebuilt the road, allowing mail and garbage services to finally be restored.

Storms and tides continue to eat away at the displaced land. Dead trees fall onto the beach. The steel rails of the old man's house jut out over the eroding land.

Life continues, the evidence of the trauma slowly erased. The catastrophic "geologic event," the mighty chunk of land that moved, affected the lives of many people, but none so profoundly as the young man on the bluff and the elderly gentleman who had lived below him at the beach.

*The old man's house,
perched above the beach.*

The young man's house, on top of the bluff.

A Boy and His Dog

Frozen on the sidewalk above the beach, he leans
against the sturdy metal fence.
His perpetual gaze seeks
foraging gray whales in Saratoga Passage.
A dog rests at the boy's feet,
a ball endlessly clenched in his teeth.
Years of petting gives the pooch's coat
a polished patina.
They wait.

The forever teen wears a debonair top hat
on a Langley Mystery Weekend.
In touristy July, his jaunty pal
sports a bow tie of red, white, and blue.
Festive autumn pumpkins
cluster near the stationary figures.
A knitted scarf adorns the boy's neck
in chill December.
They celebrate.

Captivated visitors sidle up beside the boy
and adopt his wistful pose.
Sticky-handed children
climb upon the canine's beckoning back.
Strangers snuggle close
and shout, "Take a picture!"
"Oh, come on, take one of all of us
together."
They smile.

A Boy and His Dog
Georgia Gerber, Sculptor
Langley, 1986

Miko Johnston

Miko Johnston is the author of the historical fiction series A PETAL IN THE WIND, as well as a contributor to anthologies published by Sisters In Crime and Whidbey Island Writers Association. Miko first contemplated a writing career as a poet at age six. That notion ended four years later when she found no 'help wanted' ads for poets in the Sunday NY Times classified section, but her desire to write persisted. After graduating from New York University, she pursued a career as a journalist before switching to the more believable realm of fiction. Miko lives on Whidbey Island in Washington (the big one).

Senior High

"Package for you, Meredith."
The nurse's aide hands me a small box sent from
Miami. I open it, wondering what it could be. Inside I
find a shard of pottery and know why it's been sent to
me.

On my dresser sits a photograph taken sixty years
ago, of four young women out for a night of fun in
Manhattan. With tears in my eyes, I place the shard
there, beside the other two pieces, as my mind drifts
back to a rainy spring afternoon in 2015....

Silence has engulfed our limousine since the
ferry. My jaw hurts from clenching it. To relax as we
head north toward a place called Coupeville, I
concentrate on the endless countryside passing by –
was that a pink mailbox marked, 'Love Letters
Only?' The journalist in me thinks of interviewing
the owner; thirty-two years of marriage makes me
wonder if it's an expression of romance or fantasy.

I've been on Whidbey Island less than twenty
minutes and frankly, little of it charms, least of all
this forced reunion with my traveling companions.
Robin, still the queen of everything, and Cam, who's
done nothing but carp and snipe since we all arrived
at SeaTac Airport. I haven't seen them in forty years
and I'm beginning to think that's not long enough. I
need a distraction from these two. I peek into the
cooler and brighten when I see a bottle of wine. Oh, a

painfully bad supermarket Riesling. I put it back unopened, prompting Cam to shake her head.

Robin, sitting next to me, appears serene in her oversized sweater, pleated midi skirt and flat-heeled boots as she gazes into the distance. Giant purse and imitation leather embossed box lie by her feet, knit gloves passive in her hands. Miss Perfect has aged well.

Opposite Robin sits Cam, squirming, busy as a squirrel in autumn. Scrolling through her phone, studying each entry like it's important business. A nomad groupie until she aged out, she delivers mail, for heaven's sake. Given her skin, darkened from decades of Miami sun, and her once black hair now white from root to tip, she looks like a photonegative of her younger self. Great, she's caught me staring. She shifts in her seat and the leather upholstery creaks so loud we all flinch.

Robin nudges me. "So Meredith, I'd heard from Linda that you retired."

"I did, last month."

Robin looks ready to say more, but doesn't. Thirty-eight years running a preschool has taught Robin forbearance.

Silence returns. So does the ache in my jaw.

Robin crosses her legs. Her boot heel knocks her purse against the box, which slides into my ankle. I push the box away with my foot, earning one of Robin's notorious facial reproaches. To avoid it I turn to Cam. "How's your leg? Linda had mentioned you fell on your route a while back."

"Fine," Cam mutters, her eyes never leaving her phone.

Once again silence enfolds us like an itchy blanket. Robin picks pretend lint from her gloves. Cam continues to scroll through her phone. I want to turn away, but I feel compelled to watch, as when passing a traffic accident. My sigh provokes another scowl from Robin.

She takes an audible breath and calms. "Look at us, sitting together and ignoring each other. Thanks to Linda we used to be friends. Why aren't we talking?" Robin turns to me. "Meredith, what's holding you back?"

"Play nice, boys and girls, or teacher will get mad," Cam sasses.

"I'm...." Robin pauses. "Cam, do you still hike? If Meredith does—"

"Don't arrange play dates for us, okay?" Cam's finger flicks up her phone screen as she scrolls.

"I was going to say I like to hike, too!" Robin sputters. "Why are we having so much trouble talking to each other?"

Time to unfurl my sarcasm and let it wave. "I don't know, let's ask Linda." I open the box, pick up the urn from its satin-lined interior, and hold it up. "Linda, why are we having so much trouble talking to each other?"

"That's not funny, Meredith." Robin turns into an angry mom meme. "Put her back, now."

"Get over it. We were never close." Cam pockets her phone in her jeans. "We all loved Linda, and forty years ago we hung out together and got high, but that's not friendship. That's partying." Then she shakes her head. Again.

"So we weren't BFFs," Robin concedes, "but I

remember us having fun back then."

Cam snickers. "How hard is it to have fun when you're stoned?"

She's right, though I wouldn't give Cam the satisfaction of saying it. Truth be told, Linda was the linchpin; we all stayed close to her, but not each other. After I entered grad school I never had more than a Christmas card relationship with them.

The limousine stops at a red light. Outside I see two men walking their bicycles across a pedestrian bridge that spans the highway.

"You must still," Robin says to Cam.

"Still what?"

"Get high."

"Nah, quit that years ago. Can't work for the Postal Service if you're a stoner. You?"

"Joe and I did occasionally, until I got pregnant with Danny. What about you, Meredith?"

"I smoked my last joint on my thirtieth birthday, then I met über-straight Marc and never thought about it, until now. It's funny. All my friends used to take drugs to get high. Now they take them to avoid getting high – blood pressure, cholesterol, blood sugar."

The light changes to green. Our limo turns right as the sun ducks behind a cloud bank.

"Did Linda tell either of you why we had to do this on Whidbey Island?" I ask.

"All I know is this is what she wanted, and it's the only reason I'm here," Cam says.

I hope we're not going much farther. I crave a break from these two, alone in my room before dinner. A glass of good wine wouldn't hurt, either.

The limo stops at an historic Victorian 'painted lady,' the bed and breakfast where Linda had arranged for us to stay. The proprietor shows us to our rooms upstairs. Cam claims the single with a bathroom adjacent. Robin and I settle for the two rooms opposite Cam's, with a shared bathroom between. I text updates to Marc as the proprietor hands out keys before going downstairs.

Cam mentions, "You know pot's legal in Washington."

Robin fumbles with her antique key. "So what?"

Cam unlocks her door. "Just saying."

"You think Linda brought us together here so we could get high again?"

I turn on the Tiffany-shade floor lamp near the stairway. "I doubt it. She spent her last hours planning every detail of this trip – airfare, limo, lodging."

Cam drops her backpack inside her room. "Even a bottle of wine for Meredith to turn her nose up at."

I won't be provoked. "I think if Linda had intended for us to get high she'd have left a joint in the limo."

Robin agrees. "We wouldn't know where to buy the stuff."

"It's sold in licensed cannabis shops throughout the state in community-approved locations," I explain.

Under her breath Cam mutters, "Aren't we the know-it-all."

She's starting to tick me off. "I covered the West Coast for my network."

Robin flashes her palm, teacherlike, to silence us.

"Cam, you're insulting when you call Meredith a know-it-all, and Meredith, I heard a little snobbery in your answer to Cam."

"Robin, I'm not four, so stop treating me like one of your preschoolers." I unlock my door. "God, I hope they have some decent wine here."

"You see, she is a snob." Cam shakes her finger at me. "Watch, she'll make us go from restaurant to restaurant because none of them will be good enough for her."

"No, let's eat whatever swill you choose." I fight the urge to smack her hand away.

"Stop it, both of you," Robin snaps. "Maybe getting high would improve your mood."

Silence again, but it feels different this time.

I close my room door. "You want to?"

I don't hear anyone say no.

"How can we find one of these cannabis shops?" asks Robin.

"Ask the owner," suggests Cam.

Robin's not comfortable with that. "Think they're listed in the Yellow Pages?"

"Join the twenty-first century." I pull out my iPhone. "Hey Siri, where can I buy marijuana?"

"One option is 'High On 20' in Oak Harbor. Do you want that one?"

We ask the limo driver to park at the bottom of a hill while we climb up to High On 20, located in a semi-deserted strip mall set back from Highway 20. Before we enter, Robin grabs Cam and me by our sleeves.

"Jeez, I'm jumpy. I can't get it in my head that pot's legal."

Cam pulls from Robin's grasp. "Better than roaming around Greenwich Village to buy a nickel bag from someone you hope isn't a narc."

Robin opens her wallet. "Or trying to score a lid from sleazy Dick." She counts her cash. "Uh-oh. You think they take credit cards?"

They're stalling. "Are we doing this, or not?"

We enter a tiny lobby, where a woman in a Seahawks sweatshirt guards the facility behind a glass-partitioned booth. "I'll need to see your ID's."

Robin whispers to us, "I didn't think anyone would have to find out." She asks Ms. Seahawks, "Why do you need them?"

"No one under twenty-one can enter."

"You really think we —"

"I don't, lady, but the law says we have to check everyone."

After we show our ID's, the woman hands us each a senior discount coupon and buzzes us into a stark shop. Two clerks sit behind a long glass counter with jars of cannabis products and paraphernalia on display. It looks like a cross between a tobacco shop and a low-rent jewelry store. I browse the hand-blown bongs while Cam picks up a laminated product list from the counter. "Holy cow – they got a friggin menu."

Robin puts on reading glasses and squints to see the fine print. "Look at all these brands. 'Chem Dawg,' 'Silver Haze.' Never heard of them."

"Do they have 'Maui Wowie?'" asks Cam.

"No, but there's something called 'Blue

Hawaiian.'"

A young woman with a spiderweb tattoo on her neck greets us. "Can I help you?"

Robin pulls Cam to the counter. "We'd like to buy some marijuana, please."

"How much would you like?"

They look at each other. Robin whispers into Cam's ear and Cam nods.

"Can we get a lid?"

"All our vials come with lids, ma'am."

Robin throws up her hands and walks away from the counter muttering, "I'm sorry, I can't buy dope from a dealer who calls me 'ma'am.'"

The older guy behind the counter translates for us. "She wants an ounce. We sell by the gram now."

I ask Spider-Girl, "Can you explain the difference between the various products?"

"All of our strains are organically grown in the region. The staff samples everything we sell so we can make recommendations. You can choose according to the THC content, scent, taste, or the effect you'd prefer." She reaches under the counter and pulls out a jar labeled 'Blueberry Kush.' "Take a whiff of this." She removes the lid and lets me smell it.

"It does smell like blueberries and..." I sniff it again. "I'm getting a little mint, no, menthol. Eucalyptus?"

"And hay, right? This will provide a pleasant, mellow high. Great for chilling out with friends." She puts the jar back and brings out one called 'Sour Diesel.' "What about this?"

I take a whiff. "Smoky. And I'm getting a little

grape in the background."

The clerk nods. "It's an Indica strain, great if you're having trouble sleeping." She brings out one more jar. "And this?"

I breathe in and cough. "Skunkweed! God, that brings back memories. But this one's got some spice to it, kind of pumpkin pie-like."

"This is 'Apollo 13.' It's good for energy, motivation, and creative thought."

"It's sort of like choosing a wine."

"Good analogy."

"I may be getting a contact high." I fan my face and ask the others, "So, one gram of...what?"

Cam shrugs. "They all sound good. Robin?"

"I like blueberries."

Back in Coupeville, we ask the limo driver to drop us at Front Street, an area of quaint shops, restaurants, and walkways along the waterfront.

I check my phone app. "There are several good restaurants in town."

"What's wrong with pizza?" Cam asks.

"I don't eat pizza."

Robin interrupts. "Enough. You're never going to agree. Besides, we have big plans for this evening, remember?"

We forego dinner at a restaurant and instead wander along Front Street down to the wharf, where we stop to gape at a snow-capped mountain skirted with clouds. Continuing uphill, we find a gourmet shop for cheese, crackers, and chocolates. Goodies in hand, we return to the inn.

Robin unlocks her door and we enter her room, the largest of the three. She drops her purse on the bed and takes off her sweater; she looks half her size without it. "I snatched souvenir matches from Toby's Tavern. Figured we'd need them." Robin places them on the antique bedside table.

Cam smacks her forehead. "We forgot to buy rolling paper. How're we gonna smoke this?" She unbuttons her jacket, revealing her vintage 'New York Dolls' tee shirt underneath, signed by the band when they played the Hotel Diplomat in '72.

"Bummer," says Robin. "What can we use?"

I spot the antique glass knob on the bathroom door. "I can rig a pipe out of that doorknob if I can unscrew it."

"This I gotta see." Cam digs into her backpack for a Swiss Army knife and unsnaps the screwdriver for me.

"Perfect. Now I need a straw, – wait! Skip the doorknob. I can make a chillum pipe out of foil and an empty toilet paper roll."

"I got a nearly empty one in my bathroom." Cam races out and brings it to me.

I unspool the remaining toilet paper. The cardboard roll is much shorter and wider in diameter than the last time I did this. "I'll need the mini sewing kit in my bag."

Robin hands me my purse.

"Found it. Robin, take the foil off two of those chocolates."

She rummages through the sack. "Dark or milk?"

"Doesn't matter."

Robin pops the chocolates in her mouth before

giving me the wrappers.

I cover one end of the roll with a foil and tie it with thread. Using the Swiss Army knife's scissors, I cut a half-inch-wide hole near the foil-covered end and press the second foil into it, forming a bowl, and punch thirteen holes in the bottom with my sewing needle.

Cam looks impressed. "You're like friggin MacGyver, girl."

That makes me smile. "I'd forgotten you don't swear. It's refreshing. Everyone in L.A. is so foul mouthed."

Robin nods. "New York, too."

I hold up my creation. "Done. Let's load her up."

Robin breaks apart the gram chunk of Kush over a brochure. "Clean, no seeds." She puts a piece in the foil bowl. "Who gets the first hit?"

"It was your idea, Robin," I say.

"But you made the pipe."

Cam snatches the matches from the nightstand. "Gimme that chillum. Better open the window first."

"You feel anything?" Other than throat irritation, I don't. "Maybe we need to smoke more."

Cam takes another big hit until her eyes bulge. She presses her lips together so hard they disappear. I know that look. She's fighting the urge to cough, but won't let on that she can't handle it. She finally exhales, but it's left her bug-eyed and pacing like a caged wildcat. "This place has a no-smoking policy. We're gonna get in trouble."

I take another toke before passing the pipe to

Robin. "That applies to tobacco. This smidgeon of pot isn't going to be noticeable."

"They'll think we ate blueberries." Robin takes a hit and offers the chillum to Cam, but she refuses it.

"My heart's racing and I feel...funny. I can't explain it." Her head darts like a cat following a laser toy.

"Are you feeling paranoid?" Robin asks.

Cam's eyes grow in horror. "I am now!" She buttons up her coat and scoots to the side of the bed against the wall, hugging her knees to her chest. We give her a moment to calm down before continuing.

I take another hit from the pipe and that once-familiar euphoric buzz revisits. Déjà vu washes over me as I hyper-focus on things I hadn't noticed, like a crack in the ceiling. Or maybe a rabbit hole, for suddenly it feels like New York 1974 and we're in Linda's seedy studio apartment in the East Village. Bowie's 'Ziggy Stardust' provides the soundtrack....

"No bogarting."

I snap back when Robin takes the pipe from my hand and lights it.

Cam nestles into the mass of chenille bed pillows, mouthing silent words while her eyes swivel. She's blitzed.

Robin exhales smoke. "All gone. Where's the ashtray to empty this?" She smacks her forehead. "Duh, no-smoking room."

Two sets of eyes fix on me. "Hey, I figured out the pipe."

"Dump it in the trash," Robin suggests, but Cam warns, "What if it's still burning? We could start a fire."

Robin considers the fireplace, but I point to the glass facing.

"Then where can we put the ashes?" Robin wonders.

It comes to me immediately and I start laughing.

Robin's stoned, so it takes a moment for her to catch on. "Oh, no. You can't do that, no, no, no. Cam, tell her she can't."

But Cam's fallen asleep.

"C'mon. It's the perfect solution," I insist. "And she'd love it."

"Yeah, she would. Okay." Robin takes the ceramic urn out of the box and places it on the bedside table. She slowly lifts the lid and peers inside. "Hey Linda, join the party."

Robin drags a wing chair from across the room to the desk and melts into it like grilled cheese. "Remember that thing you did at Linda's with the Chiclets?"

I do, but say, "No." I sit in the desk chair. We'd left Cam sleeping and moved to the other side of the room.

Robin leans the cardboard pipe against a paperweight on the desktop. "Let's save the rest for Cam when she wakes up so she won't throttle us."

I turn on the exhaust fan in the bathroom and return to Robin's room. A snort from Cam startles us when she rolls over in bed. Robin and I snicker.

I cover my mouth so Cam won't hear me. "Some party girl."

"You can't get into raves with an AARP card,"

Robin whispers, and we both erupt into giggles. Luckily Cam sleeps through it.

Robin drops the matchbook on the desk. "Doing this feels weird, like going back in time. Sometimes it feels like yesterday, then it seems like ancient history."

"And for me, splintered memories. A while ago, I found myself in Linda's apartment the last time we all partied together, the night before I enrolled at NYU."

"When would you have had time to party, between school and work? Same with Joe and me."

"Did you stay in touch with Cam after she left New York?"

Robin strokes the urn. "Only through Linda. I often thought about calling her, but then...."

Like me. "I sent Cam a condolence letter when her parents died, but she never responded."

"Linda told me Cam called her day and night for weeks afterward, crying and ranting."

I well up. "Linda could give comfort and encouragement to everyone but herself." Robin takes my hand and gives it a squeeze. I place my other hand on hers.

Fiery light draws my attention to the window, where a blood-orange sky heralds sunset. "Must be close to seven."

Robin checks her watch. "Try eight-thirty."

"That late?" I reach into our goodie bag for a bottle of water. "Want some?"

"Sure."

I pour two glasses as Robin tucks her feet under her.

"Great profile on Marc in *The Wall Street Journal*. Did you get to meet the President?" She takes a sip of water.

"Not this one."

"You miss reporting?"

"Sometimes," I lie, but truth serum lurks in this grass. "My retirement wasn't exactly voluntary."

"I figured." Robin stretches out in her chair like melted mozzarella. I need food.

"That's what's great about owning your own business," she says. "Job security."

"When will you retire?"

"Never. Love my work too much—"

Cam pops up from the bed like a jack-in-the-box. "You talking about me?"

"Not anymore. Now we're talking about me." Robin holds out the pipe for Cam. "We saved you some."

"Nah. I didn't enjoy the high."

"Guess you're not the wild child anymore." Robin chuckles as she offers me the pipe. I decline.

"So what?" Cam snarls. "You gotta get high to be a rebel?"

"No, I only meant—"

"I know what you meant. At least I had fun."

"And I didn't?"

I shush them. "Stop fighting. You'll upset Linda." I point to the open urn on the table.

Cam slides out of Robin's bed. "What did you do?"

"Partied with Linda one last time." I tap the remaining grass into the urn and replace the lid. "Now she's ready to be scattered on the water."

Cam sits on the edge of the bed. I wait for the snide remark, but instead she gets teary. She stares at the urn for a moment, then wipes her eyes. "I'm going to my room to crash." She grabs her backpack and hurries out.

"We should get some sleep, too."

Robin yawns. "The high is wearing off. I'll use the bathroom first."

She closes the door, leaving me alone in her room. Maybe it's the grass, but the urn beckons me. I stare at all that's left of my dearest friend and I don't get why she wanted her remains to be scattered near Deception Pass. She spent one night on Whidbey forty years ago during a cross-country trip.

I whisper, "Linda, why'd you bring us here?"

"You say something?" Robin asks as she emerges from the bathroom.

"Just good night." I go to my room and close the door, wondering if I'll sleep.

I spring awake minutes before my seven o'clock wake-up call. Fat raindrops tap against the windows like thrumming fingers. I hear the shower running; Robin's already up. I fold the clothing I'd left draped over a chair, then open my luggage. The silk pantsuit I brought doesn't seem appropriate. I'll wear my airplane outfit: a sweater long enough to cover the pricy nametag on my jeans, a pashmina, and running shoes.

Robin knocks on our connecting door before poking her head in. "Morning. Bathroom's all yours."

The three of us meet downstairs in the sunroom for breakfast. Cam heads for the sideboard, where a coffeepot awaits. She pours herself a cup, then asks us, "You want some?"

"Please," Robin says, holding out her cup.

"No thanks." I pour a cup of hot water from a thermos and take a sip. Cam's watching, so to curb any headshaking I explain, "I can't tolerate the acid."

"So no pizza. But you can drink wine?"

"Only certain types."

The proprietor enters, informing us that our limo has arrived. After we finish breakfast, Robin brings Linda's urn downstairs, and with umbrellas in hand we leave for Deception Pass. Except for the rhythmic swish of windshield wipers, we sit side by side in silence, but it doesn't feel tense like yesterday. It's comforting, almost meditative. Picturesque farms, stands of scotch broom, and meadows strewn with wildflowers rush past; the ocean winks through trees, and despite the rain I find myself captivated by the beauty of Whidbey Island in mid-May.

The limo stops at a succession of lights as we drive through Oak Harbor. Robin smiles and waves at High On 20 as we pass.

"Do either of you know how we're supposed to do this?" I ask.

Cam shrugs. "Do you?"

I shake my head. "See, I don't know it all."

"That's for sure," blurts Robin. "She doesn't even remember the Chiclets thing."

Cam slaps her thighs. "No, you have to! I spent the next five years trying to do it and never could."

"Huh?"

"Don't you remember that summer when Linda got laid off and we partied at her place every night after work?" Robin asks. "One time she passed out a package of Chiclets to ward off dry mouth, and later you pulled out two perfectly formed pillows of gum from your mouth and announced, 'Look, everybody. I pushed my pieces back together.'"

Cam nods with recollection. "So tell us how you did it."

I burst out laughing. "You never figured it out?"

They both stare blankly at me.

"I didn't chew them. I held them in my mouth and sucked the sugar coating off."

"That was mean!" Cam exclaims, but her indignation changes to laughter.

Robin laughs, too. "No, that was funny."

"Yeah, that was funny," Cam agrees. "You were always funny."

"I had the humor. Robin had the fortitude, and you had the balls."

Cam blows on her fingernails and rubs them on her shoulder. "Still do."

The strip malls disappear. We pass a pair of military jets on display. Farther along a farm stand's billboard proclaims: *Reopening Memorial Day*. We enter a forested area and our limo slows as the speed limit drops from fifty to forty to thirty. The rain has turned to drizzle.

And then we cross a bridge overlooking fir-covered bluffs to our left, channeling water toward the open sea. There's an inlet with verdant islands and peaks rising from the water to our right. An almost reverential silence envelopes us, as if any sound would disturb the view. I've traveled throughout this country, throughout the world, yet I can't think of another place more beautiful than this. I'm astounded.

"It's breathtaking," observes Robin, and Cam agrees.

The limousine uses an access road to make a U-turn. We drive over the bridge again, then the vehicle turns right and follows a narrow road downhill, past stands of trees and lush greenery, to a parking lot. The rain has stopped.

The limo driver directs us to a trailhead. Robin cradles the urn and we follow the trail over a wooden footbridge, through a copse of trees, and past a small knoll dotted with a rainbow of wildflowers. With hands clasped, we help each other clamber over driftwood logs until we reach the beach. Above to our right stands the bridge, to our left the ocean. I sit on a log to pick damp leaves from my soles, breathing in the scent of salt spray mixed with the tang of sea grass. Ahead, scallops of foam-edged water touch the shore and retreat, moistening the gray-brown sand with every lap. Clouds billow across a pale gray sky with darker streaks to the north, a monochromatic background for two eagles swooping not twenty feet from my head. I begin to understand why *here*.

Robin sets the urn in the sand, lifts her arms and spins around like a little girl. "I can't believe this place."

Cam sits on the sand, head down. "I can't believe she's really gone," she murmurs, pain riddling her face.

I rub Cam's back. "That's because Linda always felt closest to you. She once told me you led the life she would have liked if she had the guts to do it."

She looks at me, not with hostility, but surprise. "That true?"

"Ask her yourself." I gesture toward the urn.

Instead she rises and dusts sand from her jeans. "Let's do this."

Robin picks up the urn. "We should each say something."

"I'd like to pick some wildflowers first." I collect a handful of tiny daisy-like flowers from the knoll. Robin picks purple blossoms while Cam watches.

Robin uncovers the urn. "Who wants to start?"

"You should," Cam tells her.

Robin raises the vessel. "Linda, I'll miss our weekly Friday night dinners, celebrating the holidays together, gabbing on the phone. You were like family to Joe, the kids, and me, and we're all going to miss 'Aunty Lin.'"

Cam takes the urn. "Linda, you were my best friend, the only one who understood why I did the crazy things I did."

Her voice cracks. She pauses to clear her throat.

"You never criticized me or told me I was wrong, even when I was. But I'm still mad at you for leaving me." She says it calmly, and as she passes the urn to me her body relaxes. I think she's reached the final stage of grief – acceptance.

I'm speechless. Her last remark knocks what I'd planned to say from my head. Something straightforward and succinct, like the obits I'd written during my career. But what Cam said reminds me the voice we need most now is missing, and has been missing throughout this trip.

Linda's.

Who she was to us, and how we could never be that for her. She found a way to bring us together. Like those cyclists crossing the bridge in Coupeville, maybe I can find a way for us to bond together for Linda, help her cross over.

I stare at the urn for inspiration and the words tumble out. "Thank you, Linda, for all that you did to enrich my life. You befriended me when I was alone, but 'friend' doesn't begin to describe it. You gave me hope when I felt hopeless, offered encouragement when the universe toppled on me, lifted my spirits when setbacks crushed them. You made my life – all of our lives – so much richer by being a part of it."

I didn't expect to cry, let alone as much as I am. Cam and Robin put their arms around me until I regain my voice.

"You may be gone from this earth, but you are not gone from our memory, or our hearts, or our lives, which you did so much to shape. Rest in peace, Linda, and may the next world treat you better than this one did."

I turn the urn over the water and let some of the ashes sprinkle out. I pass the urn to Robin, who pours more out. She then passes it to Cam, who empties the urn.

Robin tosses her flowers in the water. "Purple was your favorite color."

"I've always thought daisies were the most unpretentious flower. They remind me of you." I drop my wildflowers in one by one.

The ashes slowly merge with the rushing water, the flowers float away on the current. Then an idea seizes me. I smash the urn against a rock.

"Why'd you do that?" cries Cam.

"So we can each take a piece with us, as a memento of Linda's last journey, and our part in it."

We each select a piece and hold our shard near our hearts as I take a selfie of the three of us.

"What about the rest?" Robin asks me.

"Toss them."

"No, we can't, it wouldn't be right," insists Cam.

"Why?" asks Robin. "It's not Linda's home anymore."

I look across the channel and up toward the bridge. "No. This is where she'll live from now on, very happily, I suspect, in this extraordinary place…"

Linda, then Robin, and now Cam. They're all gone now, as is that selfie of us at the beach.

I move the shards around until their arrangement pleases me; side by side, each comfortable in its spot. There they shall remain until it's my turn to join the others, whenever that will be.

Until then, I'm the keeper of memories.

Whidbey Winter

January falls and Whidbey holds its breath
paused between what was and what is soon to be
autumn pleasures long gone spring still far away
on these darkened days I huddle by a fire
where I can enjoy the silent solitude
gazing out upon the drama of the shore

texturings of gray imbues the winter sky
shuffled by the wind that warns of coming rain
no one walks the rocky surface of the beach
gathering unbroken clam and cockle shells
playing hide and seek in driftwood teepee huts
pretending to defend the realm from pirate ships

rushing waves deposit logs along the beach
moving rocks and crushing mussel shells to sand
long ago blue herons left the water's edge
only ducks and scoters brave the winter cove
prey to eagles hunting for a morning meal
I can watch their aerial ballet for hours

soon the days will lengthen and the darkness ease
orchard trees will leaf out and the herbs rebloom
but for now I'll watch the winter storms play out
awed by January's gift of quiet time

A Whidbey Island Tail,
er, Tale

*This story is true; the names have been changed
to avoid humiliation or lawsuits.*

Once upon a time, which in this case means a
week and a half ago, there lived in the state of
Washington, on an island called Whidbey, a woman
nigh on three score named Miss Bloomfield, who
sought solace and amity from all. A quirky lass, each
day she would sit by the front window of her home,
ready to embrace what life had to offer, with a coffee
mug in one hand and what she called a thermos in the
other to refill her cup. While drinking coffee all day
had become common practice amongst the
inhabitants of this island, after her morning cup Miss
Bloomfield switched to a yeastier brew than could be
found in the local coffee shops.

She exhibited a fastidious attachment to the
traditions of her native land. She would not begin
filling her mug until the afternoon, for she grew up in
an East Coast city to be left unnamed. She continued
to observe her homeland's ritual of waiting until 5:00
p.m. before imbibing, which fortuitously coincided
with 2:00 p.m. West Coast time. Only later did Miss
Bloomfield conclude that the actual custom entailed
waiting until the *afternoon*, which to her meant *after
noon*, or 9:00 a.m. on Whidbey Island.

With her filled mug in one hand and her trusty
six-pack, um, thermos in the other, she'd observe the

world through her window as long as her eyesight permitted, which usually failed around lunchtime. Then following a short nap, she'd awake refreshed, pull herself up from the floor, and take her place in the chair by the front window, sipping from her refilled mug until either darkness, or she, fell.

On this particular spring day, Miss Bloomfield had gotten a pre-dawn start to her routine thanks to nearby Keyhill Farm's new rooster. After a breakfast of toast and coffee, which in this case was Folgers instant, she sat with her daily accoutrements and gazed outside. Hours passed. Birds flew by. A few alit on straggly bushes yearning to be pruned. A doe and two fawns tramped across her lawn, undisturbed by bees harvesting nectar from the multitude of dandelions. Later, a rabbit paused to nibble clover before dashing off. All the while she sat and drank her yeasty brew, then popped open a new thermos to refill her mug. Again.

Looking outside shortly before nap time, she spied a most unusual creature trotting across her driveway, the size of a deer, but it wasn't a deer. She rubbed her eyes to make sure they weren't lying to her. They weren't. She gawked at the magnificent beast, wondering what it could be. White as heaven, with a form similar to a horse, but this was no horse. Its musculature appeared much smoother, its mane sleek as a waterfall. What astounded Miss Bloomfield most? She saw two horns protruding from its head. Gasping and gaping, she dialed the local sheriff on her landline. At the recording she pressed two and waited to be connected to dispatch.

***

"Sheriff, it's Miss Bloomfield again," the dispatch officer said with a grin.

"What line?"

"Two."

The sheriff picked up line two. "Hello, Miss Bloomfield. What can I help you with today?"

"Sheriff, ya gottuh get here right away."

He could hear her slurring her words. Not even eleven yet. "What is it this time?"

"I got me a unicorn in my yard."

"A unicorn," he repeated.

"Yeah, an not jus any unicorn, but a rare, magical white unicorn, with two horns, Sheriff. Two!"

"Okay, Miss Bloomfield, I'll take care of it immediately."

"You will?"

"You bet."

As soon as Miss Bloomfield hung up, the sheriff dialed another number.

"Keyhill Farms."

The sheriff let out an audible breath. "Doris, looks like your white mule escaped again."

Awaiting Spring
in Meerkerk Gardens

Rhododendron buds in May
shiver in the morning chill
plump suspended and compact
like pursed lips ready for a kiss
sleeping eyes before first light
they hold fast and refuse to burst.
   They're late

The sun is meek, cowered by
the last of winter's lingering breath
it can't pry open slumbering buds
no royal purple, golden maize
fiery red or vibrant pink
to interrupt the ceaseless green
of rhodie bushes yet to bloom.
   I wait

Karen Rothboeck

Karen has lived on Whidbey Island since 1984. The three short stories appearing in the 2015 anthology, Write Around Whidbey, are her first published works in a book. For ten years, she contributed articles and a monthly book review column to The Coupeville Examiner (later The Whidbey Examiner). She is currently teaching yoga and writing a science fiction novella.

One-Hour Islandizing

Bob rapped on the heavy iron door and heard a hollow echo behind it. "What's this place called 'Switchboard' and why is it blocked off?"

"I heard it's the deepest, darkest part of Fort Casey and not safe to explore. Although, in its day I guess it made sense, having communications tucked into a space that would be protected from attack," Craig answered.

"Wouldn't you just love to go in there?"

"Well, I've been in there. When we moved here thirty years ago, it was still open to the public. The kids loved to come here with flashlights and explore everywhere. They said this was the scariest place at the whole fort."

"It almost seems like it's still being used." Bob pointed to a sweep of clean concrete beneath his feet. "This makes it look like the door's been swung open and closed recently."

"I don't know what caused that mark, but I'm going to say it hasn't been opened unless maybe for some sort of maintenance."

"Yeah, maybe that's all it is. But maybe your kids were right. I get a creepy feeling just standing in this spot. It's like somebody's watching us, maybe the ghosts of some of those WWI soldiers who were stationed here."

***

Deep in the bowels of Switchboard, Dr. Angus Silberstein leaned across a desk for a closer look at the screens fed by the surveillance cameras. "Anything I need to worry about?" He was wearing a stained lab jacket and scratching his head, leaving his halo of unruly hair looking even wilder than it had a moment ago.

Lenny leaned back in his chair, the springs squeaky. "Nah, just two old geezers. Probably history buffs. They were pretty focused on the door for a minute there, but it looks like they're moving on."

The doctor hoped opening the big old iron door hadn't been a mistake. "I didn't like having to open that door last night, but I couldn't think of another way to get our big new piece of equipment in here."

Lenny moved his attention away from the screen and back to the doctor. "Yeah." He slowly worked on the piece of gum in his mouth. He really didn't care too much about new equipment. He really didn't care much about anything other than getting a paycheck.

"How are our patients?" The doctor was pretty patient himself as he waited for Lenny to process the question and formulate an answer.

"Next load's due in any minute." Lenny pointed at one of the other screens, which showed an ambulance backing up and two emergency medical technicians unloading someone on a stretcher. The area to the sides and front of the ambulance consisted of a wet, dense thicket of Douglas fir, sword fern, and salmonberries that nearly engulfed the vehicle.

"I'd better get down there. This next hour is

likely to be chaotic."

Dr. Silberstein rushed through a maze of concrete tunnels with empty iron hooks, rust-stained walls, and ceilings adorned with an occasional small stalactite. Water puddled on the floor in places, but he had learned his route as well as a lab rat learns a maze and knew how to avoid the slippery spots.

The gurney he'd seen being unloaded from the ambulance was now being rolled across the room – the room filled with cots, the cots filled with patients. Many of them seemed disoriented or angry, and cries of "Where am I?" and "Let me go!" filled the room.

"Triage, triage," muttered the doctor as he turned to one of the harried nurses. "Who's in the worst shape here?"

A pretty young woman pushed a stray lock of hair from her face with her right hand while taking a patient's pulse with her left hand. "Maybe her," she said, pointing to her current patient.

"History?"

"Made an obscene gesture to one of our local drivers at the four-way stop on South Main."

"Get her right down to the genealogy library! She's gotta learn that when she does something like that, the driver she got mad at is probably related to at least a dozen other people here in Coupeville. No one is going to like that," he muttered.

The nurse began to get a wheelchair ready. "It gets worse, you know. The reason for that little argument was because everybody was being so polite at the intersection that no one went. Kind of a politeness standoff until she came along and ruined it."

"*Aaagh!* She should have been impressed, not mad. How about this one?" The doctor pointed to a well-dressed man in a suit and tie sitting on the edge of a cot.

"Found carrying an umbrella on a rainy day. We've confiscated it, of course. It's in the storeroom with all of the others."

"Umbrellas. Bah! Nothing hardy Pacific Northwesterners use. What about his outfit?"

"Doctor, I was planning to take him to the wax museum. Once he's seen our statue of *Homo sapiens,* variation *Whidbeyanicus,* perhaps he'll have some sense shaken into him. Next stop, the wardrobe, where we've got plenty of plaid flannel shirts and jeans."

"Tilley hat," the patient moaned. "Rolex."

A sudden commotion at the door made the doctor and nurse turn away from their patient.

Two EMT's bearing a stretcher came running in. "We need assistance, stat!"

"What seems to be the problem?" The doctor's calm demeanor was reassuring. He looked down at a young woman who was struggling against the straps on the gurney. The nurse was already wrapping a blood pressure cuff around the patient's arm.

"This is probably gonna need surgical detachment," the younger of the two attendants said, pointing at a cell phone the patient still clutched tightly in her hand.

The doctor was puzzled. "I see those all the time. She'll be fine."

"No, you don't understand. She was out walking the bluff trail at Ebey's Landing and talking on this at the same time."

The nurse stifled a gasp.

"Well, it's a shame to miss all of that beautiful scenery, but maybe she had an important call to make."

"Doc, it gets worse. Locals were hiking past her and saying 'hello' and 'how are you,' and she didn't respond. Didn't step out of the way. Blocked the trail. Report was she acted like they weren't even there."

The doctor paused to consider the case. "Did you get a look at her driver's license?"

"Yup. Out of state." The attendant shook his head sadly.

"You know, don't you, that we're short stay here? We do one-hour islandizing, but it sounds as if this woman needs intensive, long-term care."

"I want my aesthetician!" the woman was screaming at the top of her lungs. "And my publicist! And my...my hot yoga instructor and my pedicurist! I am in a state of disbelief that she can't work me in tomorrow."

Her phone rang, or rather, produced a braying version of an old Tom Jones song. Everybody leaped back in shock.

"Hypodermic," the doctor whispered to the nurse as he rummaged through the drug cart and handed her a vial. "Three cc's. It should be easy as pie, since the patient's already fairly oblivious."

The woman slapped at the sting from the needle as if it were a mosquito. Once she started looking around, her attention was drawn to the ancient concrete walls of the Switchboard and the ocher and lime green stains etched on the concrete walls. "My god. Who is your decorator?" She shivered. "He should be consigned to hell. By the way, do youuu neeeed...a...naaaaaammme..." She slumped like a melting marshmallow back onto the bed.

"She goes straight back to her home state," the doctor ordered. "Get her out of here before she wakes up again."

Silberstein turned toward the ambulance bay as he heard the doors slide open and his name being called. "Doc, look what we caught us!"

A couple of members of the security team were escorting in the same two men the doctor and Lenny had seen previously on the security cameras. The men looked a bit confused but not at all riled. They turned their heads this way and that. One of them took off his baseball cap, scratched his head, and said, "Gee, what is this place, anyway?"

The pretty nurse wandered over to take a look and giggled. "Wow, they're so authentic, they look like they could have escaped from our wax museum."

"Yes," the doctor agreed, "some veritable specimens."

"I spotted them following the ambulance tracks into the bushes. They're way too nosy for their own good," one of the guards said. "Can we keep 'em?"

"No," the doctor shook his head sadly. "You know the one-hour islandizing rules."

The guard straightened his back, closed his eyes and recited as if from memory: "Native species shall not be retained. They shall be treated under the catch-and-release protocol and returned unharmed to their habitat."

"Exactly," Silberstein affirmed. He turned to the nurse. "They'll need an amnesiac. Make it 5 cc for the smaller guy and 6 cc for the larger."

He turned to the guards. "Escort them down to the campground and plant them at one of the picnic tables there, or find their vehicle and put them back in it. Keep them under observation until they're walking and talking normally again."

A week later, Bob sat at the bar. "Boys, you wouldn't believe it," he said, sliding the bottom of his beer bottle around and around, drawing a little pool of condensation into loopy circles atop the polished wooden surface. "We were the subjects of an alien abduction."

Craig looked at him. "You don't know that. You don't remember a thing."

Bob stared him down. "No, you're the one who doesn't remember a damn thing. We were abducted."

Craig addressed the group at large. "We were poking around out at the fort. The next thing we knew we were sitting at a picnic table and someone had left us a couple of ice cold beers, caps still on."

"That still doesn't mean alien abduction."

"How else would you explain it?"

"Well, how would you explain that we walked all over that old fort another time after that and didn't find any of that stuff you say you remember – the cute nurse, the mad scientist, the security crew, the secret trails and secret doors?"

"I don't remember that second walk either. But I do seem to remember being back at that same picnic table with another two beers waiting on us."

Their listeners took a moment to ponder the story. They never really came here for the beer; they came here for the social aspect and the deep philosophical discussions. In unison, the listeners nodded their heads and all agreed with Bob. "Yup, alien abduction."

Someone from a booth in the corner stood up and walked carefully, one foot shakily in front of the other, toward the jukebox. Coins tumbled into a slot and a minute later, Kenny Rogers and Dolly Parton were crooning "Islands in the Stream."

Craig lifted his head like an alert hunting dog who had caught the sound of his quarry. "Island... islands... *islandizing*," he said. *"One-hour islandizing*. Is that the name of a song? Or, if it's not, why the heck's it stuck in my head?"

The Smiling Dog

I don't believe in half measures. Why sit at my human's feet when I can sit *on* my human's feet? And why stop at a little contact between doggy rump and human toes when a full-butt plant enables me to immobilize my owner completely?

There are days when I have to haul out my entire repertoire. There's a full-body lean which works equally well on a seated or standing human. My smile is irresistible. I show a little bit of tooth, striving for lovable, not menacing. I do tongue exercises when no one is looking, to get full extension and that happily panting appeal. I've always felt I have a particularly fine and prominent occiput, which complements the whole presentation of the smile.

Did I mention the tail thump? It's important to get a rhythm that appeals -- not so much Led Zeppelin drum solo as the sweet, gentle swish of the brushes in a 1960's jazz piece.

We golden retrievers aren't egotistical. Normally I wouldn't even mention my talents or reveal my trade secrets, but it's all preface to my current complaint: Nothing is working. Nothing.

Even the old I've-got-a-flea ploy -- where I nip at myself with my teeth and lick excessively, and generally need to be stopped by the steadying hand of my human -- isn't getting any notice.

Sigh. I do sighs well, too, by the way. They are best when accompanied by a full belly flop, eye roll with the chin flat on the floor, and the whole body radiating Weltschmerz.

But enough about me. I need to get to the subject of Pete, or more correctly, the subject of Pete and Carrie.

What can I say? I tried my best with her. She's an assault to the nostrils – all hairspray, nail polish, and apricot-scented lotion. I much prefer the smell of a man with a liver treat in his pocket.

When I say I tried, I mean I ignored the olfactory insults. I positioned my chin on her knee and gazed adoringly into her eyes. She gave me little surreptitious go-away nudges with her pedicured toes and then made a big thing of brushing dog hair off her jeans. As if I shed! As if it should matter!

Pete and Carrie would go out to dinner and leave me in charge of the fort. Pete would bring back a doggie bag for me with a corner of his steak in it. Carrie would bring back leftovers for *herself,* but it didn't hurt my feelings too much. Like you'd catch me eating tofu unless my life depended on it.

Did I mention the walks? Carrie didn't want to go to the dog park because she worried her shoes would get muddy. She didn't want to go to the river because she didn't want "to be in the car with a wet dog." She didn't even have the decency to say she doesn't "want to be in the car with *Rogue* if he's wet." Use the name, lady! Does she even know my name?

Back to Pete. Pete doesn't seem to have the same problems with Carrie that I do. He likes her tofu and he likes her painted toes. He doesn't mind walking on sidewalks instead of in parks.

There's only one place where Pete and I agree on

Carrie. And that's – pardon my English – cats. She owns a cat. There's no fooling me and my highly tuned nose. And Pete has an allergy to cats, so there's no fooling him either.

Last week they had another fight, and I'm kind of telling tales out of doggy-training school here, but it wasn't their first. I always thought I'd like to see that cat-loving hussy get tossed out of our lives, but I didn't understand the repercussions. Although in my defense, I've read dogs have a hard time with cause and effect unless one follows immediately after the other.

So let's just say when they couldn't agree on who would move in with whom, and discussion of what to do with the cat (the disgusting creature is evidently named Fluffette) rolled around, it was one of the few times I wished I could talk.

Take her straight to the pound, is what I would have said. If it weren't so "unretrieverly," I would have growled at that point too.

Carrie wanted Pete at her house, and "the dog" ... *gulp, feeling really sad here* ... "to go back to your parents." Now there's nothing wrong with Frank and Myrna, except that they're not Pete.

I'm as possessive about Pete as I am about my stuffed bunny. And my stuffed duck. And my stuffed carrot. Love to carry those around with me everywhere I go. In fact, where the heck is Bun-Bun? Gotta watch out 'cause I once heard Carrie offer to wash him. I've spent ages getting him saturated with saliva and covered in kibble bits and developing that certain rank odor I love so much.

But I'm getting distracted from my story here.

My eardrums still hurt from the way Carrie stomped out of here and slammed the door. That was a week ago, and I would have said good riddance to bad rubbish, but Pete seems to be missing her.

Like I said, none of my normal charms are doing the trick (did I mention I can balance a Milk Bone on my nose?). Even more worrisome, the time to fill the food bowl and top off the water dish comes and goes with no action. I was reduced, and I do mean reduced, to resorting to atavistic doggy behavior. I planted myself in front of the refrigerator and barked. *Open up*, I meant. I know there's a partial can of Purina with gravy in there for me. *It's mine. Woof! Woof!*

Pete wandered into the kitchen, scuffing along in his old suede mocs. *Mmm, suede mocs. Still kind of an addiction dating back to my puppyhood.* He was scratching his head like he was the one with fleas. He looked from me to the fridge as if he had no idea what the possible connection could be, and he's an engineer! With almost as much brainpower as a golden retriever.

That's when I realized desperate measures were called for. Sorry about that hanging preposition, but it's necessary. Dogs may be called, but desperate measures are called for.

I got the leash. It's a trick I've known for years. It's just another reason I've never cared much about talking. I mean, is "I need a walk" any more obvious than a dog with a leash in his mouth?

Pete did the flea-scratching thing on his head again. He didn't look as if he knew who I was, much less what the leash was for.

I trotted over to where he stood and tried my leaning trick. *Lean into that leg!* Just the way my mom taught me. *Roll those eyes upward! Big smile! Tongue out! Happy pant and now ... add the tail!*

Finally, finally Pete turned to grab his hoodie off the coat hook. He moved a painful half a mile an hour. He crammed his Mariners cap on his head with the bill and most of his hair askew. He acted like he was ready to head out the door just like that, so I had to carry his shoes over to him. I let them drop in front of him with a clunk, only the slightest trace of slobber visible at the heels.

And we were off. I could have pulled him anywhere, deli or butcher shop, if I hadn't been dealing with Pete's temporary insanity. Pete was losing weight. Pete was turning into a slob. Pete needed help.

I knew where Carrie lived. Much as I hated to do it, I dragged Pete in that direction. When he finally noticed where we were, he tried to pull me back toward home. But I'm nothing if not insistent. I dragged us up the steps until we stood before the door. I gave a joyous jump and "accidentally" rang the doorbell.

Pete tried to pull me back down the steps, but I could hear distant footfalls echoing through the house. Carrie was coming. I needed to hold Pete here. I did my famous butt-planting sit, pinning Pete to the doormat. *Wag, wag, wag.* Although we'd walked Carrie home from Pete's a few times, I'd never been inside before.

Carrie opened the door. All the normal beauty smells were gone. I detected only a soapy aroma underlain with a salty trace of tears. Her lips quivered the way mine do when Pete makes me sit and stay for that Milk Bone trick.

"Come in," she said, opening the door a bit wider. I didn't want to give Pete an option and surged into the room. A horrible hissing ensued. A twenty-pound Maine Coon cat arched her back, bared her teeth and stood her ground.

Pete had forgotten about my leash. It trailed on the ground while he stood there staring at Carrie, speaking about as much as I usually do. I wasn't about to leave and I didn't want to do anything to make Carrie or Fluffette more upset. I looked around for a place to perform a belly-flop sigh. The only place I saw was the damned cat's bed.

The bed held maybe the middle third of my body and I did a pretty good job of flattening the rest of the thing. Carrie and Pete made puppy eyes at each other. I planted my chin on the floor between my forelegs and watched them like a spectator at the U.S. Open. Boy, I love those big swaths of green with the little flagged pee poles that I see on TV.

And then Fluffette walked over. I was bracing to take one for the team. It wouldn't be the first time I'd had a swat across the nose. I still bear permanent scars from …

But never mind. Fluffette and I touched noses. She gave me a head butt. I relented a little and scrabbled to make a corner of her bed available to her.

She stalked out of the room and I thought that was the end of our close encounter, but a moment later she reappeared with a small orange ball in her mouth. She dropped it in front of me the same way she might have proudly presented Carrie with a mouse.

I smiled.

Pat Kelley Brunjes

Pat is a retired Speech and English teacher, librarian, and school administrator. She has a doctorate in Educational Leadership: Curriculum and Instruction. Her poetry has won honors from the Willamette Writers Association, the Washington Poetry Association, and the Whidbey Island Writers Association. She taught students of all ages how to read literature aloud, and coached many students to honors in Speech and Debate, including trips to the nationals. She has three books, Poetry from the Desert Floor, The Last Confession, *and* The Girls Next Door.

The Primordial Forests
of Whidbey Island

As I hike the tree-lined path
On the way to Maxwelton Creek
My eyes see the past and the future of the forest
The composition and decomposition
Brought on by time.
Decomposition from logging and weather
Damp and rancid in rain-soaked winters
But birthing lichen and moss.
As the sun peeks through the debris and
Warms the forest floor
Wild yellow violets signal new growth.
New seedlings sprout, straight as arrows
Until the maples, near that rushing creek,
Display the red and gold of fall.

To Live by the Sea

I envy those who live by the sea

Morning walks in fog and mist

The slow capturing of the warm rays of the sun

So bright the waters ripple

Like silver ribbons

Dorothy Read

Dorothy Read's writing career started with a "Curious Camera" column in a California biweekly. Developing a passion for seeing her work in print, she went on to produce social columns, humor features, short stories, and essays that have appeared in various publications over many decades. She published her book, End the Silence, in 2010. Dorothy's love of mentoring writers led her to earn a Certificate in Editing from the University of Washington in 2016. After forty years on her beloved Whidbey Island, she now operates Dorothy Read & Associates Self-publishing Services from her new home in Boise, Idaho.

Goodbye to an Old Friend

The jaws of the giant excavator reach out and pull off a chunk—a big chunk—the way we used to pull off big pieces of cotton candy at the fair. The cab of the huge machine swings around, clamped jaws outstretched, until their contents hover over the enormous black bin. The jaws release, and board and steel and glass tumble into the bin with a loud crash. The cab swings back and the jaws seek purchase on another mouthful of the shop that has been such a rich part of our life on Whidbey Island.

The Shop, always capitalized in our dialogue, served multiple functions over its nearly forty years: home, guest quarters, game headquarters, dry storage (which became not so dry in its waning years), workout gym, and hangout. Oh yes, and shop. A glorious two-story, barn-shaped structure framed up by thick poles and built to last. Three Douglas firs toppled by gale-force winds landed on it over the years; it hardly noticed.

When my husband, Dean, and I arrived on Whidbey Island in 1978, our much-anticipated plan was to build a shop on our six wooded acres and then live in it while we built our dream home out of logs harvested from our property. That didn't quite work out.

First of all, you need seasoned logs which you get in trade for your freshly cut trees plus a lot of money. Okay, we could float a small mortgage to cover the unexpected expense. But mortgage companies don't offer conventional loans on log houses. Did they think we were going to build an Abe Lincoln cabin? Our vision was for a 3,000-square-foot two-story home, elegant with vaulted ceilings and a terrazzo-floored conservatory. Well more of a glassed-in mud room, but nice! We even made a model of our dream home. The banks were not impressed: If it's made out of logs, no mortgage. Hm. We'd have to work around that. In the meantime, we could build Dean's shop and move out of our rented home which was eating into our building reserves.

Wrong again. We didn't know the county official who issued building permits was of the old school. He didn't like to see the island filling up with counterculture people who, in his view, thought they could build just any old thing and move in. Our plan might have gotten past this gatekeeper, but our new island friend, Mike, went with Dean to help him negotiate the county "ropes." Mike wore cargo shorts and logging boots and had a foot-long ponytail, clearly a counterculture human being. It didn't help that he had been lobbying for an "Owner Builder" permit that threatened this official's domain. Dean was about to experience the fallout from this flawed relationship.

The encounter went something like this:

OFFICIAL: This is a shop?

DEAN: Yes, it is.

OFFICIAL: A shop is a secondary building.

DEAN: Well, yes, I suppose that's true.

OFFICIAL: You haven't included your primary

building on this footprint.

DEAN: There is no primary building.

OFFICIAL: Well, I can't give you a permit for a secondary building if there's no primary building.

DEAN (after a moment of thoughtful regrouping): Okay, let's just call this the primary building.

OFFICIAL: We can do that, but you can only have one primary building on a lot.

DEAN: This isn't a lot; it's six acres. Plenty of room for two primary buildings.

OFFICIAL: Nope. If you call this the primary building, then when you come back to get a permit for another primary building, you won't get one.

DEAN (with no thoughtful regrouping whatsoever): DO YOU MEAN TO TELL ME...

What came next, I think, was laced with epithets I won't bother to record.

Our verve ground to a grudging halt. But the nudge it needed came when our landlord retired and wanted his house back. We decided to build the shop—without a building permit—and move ahead with our plan.

The neighbors and every relative within driving distance who could swing a hammer showed up to help. It had to be done fast in case the county building inspector showed up to slap a stop work order on us. Four sturdy walls and a barn-shaped roof were up within three weeks, all supported by our very own tall, straight logs—a pole building. The Shop! The exterior was covered with black tar paper;

clear plastic filled in the window frames; access to the sleeping loft was by ladder or by shinnying up a pole. We had indeed built "any old thing," and we moved in.

It was cold the first night of our adventure, so Dean built a fire in our stove-made-out-of-the-interior-of-a-water-heater. (Mike, the counterculture friend, was both resourceful and clever with iron work.) Ah, warming our hands as the heat began to radiate, we realized we were looking through a two-foot-high cylinder of smoke. Dean had forgotten to secure the last piece of stovepipe. But no question, the chimney drew well.

Then there was this other issue: If you don't have a permit for your building, it would be audacious to apply for a permit for a septic system. We had no plumbing. School would be on summer break in six weeks. I was the district reading coordinator; every morning I dressed for work, all the while convincing myself I could "hold it" until I got to school. That seldom happened, so I would end up out back, behind a gigantic log, trying not to douse my pumps and pantyhose.

We had running water—it ran out of the end of a hose that was hooked up to a single hose bib about a hundred feet down the driveway. It took three hoses hooked together to reach a fairly private circle surrounded by high salal and ocean spray bushes. There, we could effect a quick shower. Very quick, as temperatures were still chilly. Thankfully, we found the showers at the state park campground and learned to anticipate the timer with our quarters before the hot water shut off. During this period,

Dean and I were invited to the country club for dinner. I excused myself to visit the restroom and found a beautiful, tiled shower. Our friends at the table were probably curious when I rushed back to tell Dean, "They have SHOWERS here! Maybe we should think about joining."

It was our good fortune to have a family member who was an electrician, so we had standard, safe 110-volt wiring almost immediately. We cooked with a two-burner hotplate, a convection oven, and a rotisserie. The Sears delivery man seemed puzzled when he brought our first purchases for the new home: a state-of-the-art Sears-best refrigerator and a top-of-the-line porta-potty, guaranteed to hold forty complete uses. There was some discussion as to what constituted a complete use and who was going to keep the tally.

Within a few weeks, Dean added amenities that seemed like luxuries: a roomy, well-ventilated outhouse, water piped into the Shop, a sink, and a water heater. It was a joyful day when he brought in the bathtub and a wash basin. The walls around the bathroom area didn't go up for a few more weeks, so privacy was a problem, but not as much as spraying down, soaping up, and rinsing off with a hose out in the woods. Still no toilet. We found a Dutch door for the outhouse so we could use that time to leave the top half of the door open and enjoy the fresh air and woodland beauty which sometimes included a deer or two. To prevent human intrusion into our nature pauses, our college-aged daughter made a plaque to hang alongside the path to the outhouse. It read

"Occupied" on one side and "Seating Available" on the other.

Dean built walls around the bathroom and our bedroom space downstairs. The "great room" was definitely roomy, and the whole loft was open for company. And they came—all summer long. Only a few failed to come back a second time, those faint-hearted who couldn't deal with the open-air outhouse or a forty-complete-use porta-potty. And then there were the large carpenter ants that occasionally dropped from the twenty-foot peak of the ceiling. A direct hit could hurt, but that didn't happen very often.

It was a lark—a jolly experiment in an alternative lifestyle and after all, it would only last a short time until the house was built across the driveway. We firmed up the plans for our home and found a designer to make them official. Then the bottom fell out of the economy, the 1980 recession was on, our portfolio looked like Swiss cheese, and mortgage interest rates spiked to 17 percent. The Shop would have to be our home for a while longer—two years longer, as it turned out.

Dean installed siding over the tar paper, shingled the roof, replaced the window plastic with glass, and built flower boxes under the front windows. We raked the woods around us, cleared the pasture of seedling alders, and planted lawns and flowers. Friends and I canned fruit in the summer and fall while Dean and the other husbands kept the canning kettle boiling over a wood fire in the barbecue. I often felt like a pioneer woman presiding over a very long campout.

We hosted Thanksgivings and Christmases for friends and family. The rotisserie turned out delicious turkeys, and pumpkin pies baked just fine in the convection oven as long as they were small enough to fit. At Christmastime we nailed cedar boughs and garlands to the poles and supplied our own Christmas trees. It didn't matter how many friends and family showed up—there was always room for one more.

At last, we began to watch the new house grow across the driveway. Just before Christmas of 1983, we moved in. Dean said we'd finally gotten out of the manger and into the inn. It was scaled down a few hundred square feet, had conventional walls, and lost the terrazzo-floored conservatory. Three bathrooms housed three toilets. It was a long time before I stopped marveling at the convenience. We still had "room for one more," but extra guests had to take their chances with the big ants out in the loft.

The Shop became a shop, and over the years Dean turned out everything from heirloom rocking horses and cradles for the grandbabies to cabinetry for the house. Raucous dart games took place long into the night as the grandchildren grew older, and it was always a good place to hang out with Grandpa when something needed to be discussed. At some point exercise equipment joined the woodworking tools, and the place started to look like a gym. The loft began to take on the look of a cluttered attic more than overflow guest quarters. The clutter spread to the floor of the Shop, and Dean spent less and less time there as his health began to decline.

I lobbied for a Clean Up the Shop Weekend, but

it was beyond a weekend's effort, and whenever we tried, it always morphed into a high-spirited family party with dart games and nostalgic trips through the attic clutter. During one of those trips, the kids found some ruined treasures along with water where it didn't belong. We put a new roof on the building, but the high spirits had been dampened for good. The Shop became a ghost shop, only good for memories and for one more box of junk or piece of broken furniture. An old friend, helpless in its disrepair.

On one of his infrequent forays to the Shop, Dean spotted the sagging loft portending a serious problem. Our sons removed the flooring and shored up the interior poles which had fallen victim to dry rot. The repair gave Dean comfort in his last months, but none of us could bring ourselves to give voice to the obvious: If those poles were rotting, then others must be rotting as well. And the poles held up the Shop.

No need to go into the sad details around Dean's death or the grief that seized all of us. I found solace in my home, our home, where I could find Dean in every corner. There, I would live out my life, and there I would die, as he had, in peace. The only fly in that ointment was the Shop. There was nothing peaceful about wondering if or when it was going to fall down.

Two years slipped by and the Shop still stood. My resolve to stay on the island was still strong. And then one night during a fierce windstorm, I lay awake listening to the crack of limbs being ripped from trees and the occasional jarring thud of a whole tree downed somewhere in the woods. I was all too aware

Postscript to
"Goodbye to an Old Friend"

The Christmas after we moved into the Shop, I befriended one of my students, a 15-year-old who had already spent a year living on the streets of Houston and had Dickensian stories to tell. When this child's unkempt appearance and pungent presence prompted a private talk, I learned he was living under a tavern and eating scraps from the local restaurants' dumpsters. His mother had wakened him one fall morning to tell him the rent was paid up through the end of the month, but after that he would have to notify the authorities that he had no place to live. The rest of the family moved to England.

Child Protective Services and the sheriff's department took over, and the boy was on his way to a group foster home on the north end of the island. My heart broke for this child; Christmas was just a few days away. The authorities gave me permission to take him home through the holiday season, to give him at least one welcoming family experience before he started the next phase of his troubled life.

His story made the rounds of the school faculty and staff. Unknown to me, one of my colleagues gave his name to a local charitable organization that provided "Good Cheer" boxes of food—everything for Christmas dinner—to families in need. Imagine my surprise when a Good Cheer volunteer drove up the driveway to deliver the bountiful gift. I questioned whether he had the right address, so he checked his list and mentioned my student's name.

Ah yes, that's my student whose parents abandoned him, I explained, making sure the Good Cheer volunteer knew that my husband and I were not the needy ones. The student had gone up the road to chop wood for a neighbor, and so I accepted the charitable gift—ON HIS BEHALF, I stressed.

I had a hunch this guy wasn't buying my story as his eyes took in the exposed sheets of silver insulation lining the interior walls and ceiling of the Shop and the plywood flooring sparsely covered by area rugs. Chances are he noticed the privy out back and the tar paper still covering that side of the shop as he drove the rest of the way around the circular drive. I found a place in the refrigerator for the new turkey—beside the 20-pounder I already had—and forgot about the volunteer and his skepticism.

Twenty years later, we had a garage sale during Labor Day weekend, wrap-up time for Whidbey Island garage sales. Cars lined both sides of the road, and bargain-seekers trudged up the driveway in droves. I noticed one gentleman walking around the perimeter of the sale area, eyeing the house and grounds with obvious interest. I approached him.

"May I help you?" I asked.

"I like what you've done with this place," he said, nodding his head in what I took to be admiration. "It's very nice." I thanked him.

"I was here before—years ago," he went on. "Delivered a box of food."

The Good Cheer man!

"You just wouldn't believe the way people were

living in that place." He pointed to the Shop. "Tar paper on the outside, totally unfinished on the inside, no plumbing—they had an outhouse!"

I shook with stifled laughter but managed to stay in control. "Tsk, tsk," I said. "Imagine that!"

The Phone Booth

What the heck is a phone booth doing there? What the heck is a phone booth doing anywhere these days? Especially that one, parked at the intersection of Classic Road and State Highway 525 south of Greenbank. No businesses, no public venue or park—just a wide spot in the road. And a phone booth. What's the story?

Back in 1908 a group of Langley farmers and business owners struck up a local phone company; they didn't want any big company getting a toehold in their community. In 1953, an entrepreneur with a love of telephone companies was on the hunt for one he could afford to buy. The spunky little Whidbey Telephone Company was ready to sell, and David Henny picked it up for a mere $20,000. Good bargain, but what about the phone booth?

It seems the booth, located at Whidbey Telephone's northernmost service boundary, was installed for the benefit of Northenders who were in the steely grasp of General Telephone and Electronics. They could use the booth to save money on long-distance calls to South Whidbey. For a dime—or a quarter—someone who lived in Coupeville or Oak Harbor could run down to Classic Road to call friends to see if they'd like to come to dinner on Friday. Well maybe, but I have a different idea.

Island lore has it that David Henny went toe to toe with the giant GTE, who wanted to gobble up the whole of Whidbey. Dave stood firm. I would like to think he planted that phone booth as a signal to GTE: This Is Where You Stop.

The phone booth came to mark the geopolitical boundary between South Whidbey and The Rest of Whidbey, starting with Greenbank. "Mason-Dixon Phone Booth" is the title of Perry Woodfin's painting of it. It's true. Driving down from the north, you are in the Republic of South Whidbey when you pass the phone booth. It rains more, there aren't any oaks, and people are more apt to order quinoa.

Mason Dixon Phone Booth
Courtesy of Perry Woodfin

The phone booth was always a convenient point of reference for giving directions.

"Turn left three-tenths of a mile north of the phone booth."

"If you pass the phone booth you've gone too far. Turn around."

It was also a handy place for unexpected guests to stop and call to say they were in the neighborhood. Or to call Mom to say the game ran late.

In 1980, the phone booth served as Social Life Central to a teenage boy whose family moved up the hill on Classic Road and were on a five-month waiting list to get a phone installed. Five months! Everyone knows a telephone is the umbilical cord that nourishes a teenager's social agenda. Our son moved into the phone booth. He took his homework with him along with hearty snacks and sometimes the dog. He was recognized up and down the State Highway 525 corridor as "The Kid Who's Always in the Phone Booth." Of course he yielded the booth when someone stopped to make a call and vacated it when gale-force winds threatened to blow it down. Finally Whidbey Telephone made good on their installation, and our son was able to move back home. For years, though, wherever he went, someone was sure to ask—"Hey, aren't you the kid…?"

Over the years we heard phone booth stories. One standout was about the woman who was in labor, driving herself to the hospital in Coupeville. At Classic Road she knew she'd never make it in time, so she stopped and called an ambulance to pick her up "at the phone booth." Another was of a runaway youth hitchhiking aimlessly with no place to go. He saw the oddly placed phone booth lighting the pitch-black night and took it as a message to call home, which he did and was reunited with his family.

Then it all began to change. Cell phones made phone booths obsolete. GTE rolled into the behemoth Verizon Communications. Telephone communications morphed into a new kind of technology. Whidbey Telephone Company became the modern, tech-savvy Whidbey Telecom. The phone booth remained unchallenged through all of this until dump trucks and asphalt spreaders began to roll up the highway, making their way to Classic Road. State Highway 525 was getting a makeover and wider shoulders.

It looked like the phone booth would be retired and removed. But its neighbors on both sides of the Mason-Dixon line rallied and demanded its return. How would people know where to turn on a dark night without that little beacon to guide them? How would people know they had gone too far without that sturdy little landmark? How would anyone know when they had crossed into South Whidbey territory or The Rest of Whidbey? The community grieved. But wait!

A new phone booth appeared, modern, without the patina my son had contributed to so many years before. They installed it on the opposite corner, causing some to hit soft dirt when they made turns that had been calibrated with the old location. It sports a perky sign on its roof, "Whidbey Telecom," and it still gifts the highway with light in the blackness of a Whidbey night. Signal to GTE and Verizon: We Are Still Here!

And the phone call is now free.

Nasus Nunn

"Nasus" is the pen name for Susan Terhune Nunn. Originally from New Jersey, then southern California. Following college, she became a stewardess for United Airlines. Susan transferred to Seattle in 1959 and she married Jim in 1960. They had two sons in Washington State. Nasus wrote poetry and short stories. She was a volunteer for Beach Watchers and Admiralty Lighthouse. She wrote, "I feel I have finally found my true home and friends here on Whidbey Island."

Damp Camp Morning

We gaze out over Penn Cove's
gray cold water
huddle beneath the blue
canopy
steaming coffee mugs
warm our hands
tears of rain bring us closer
together
the local seal pup has not
greeted us as usual
the eagles and crows are
hidden and silent
a Kingfisher soon arrives
with a loud rattling call
dives for breakfast
droplets of water bounce
off the picnic table
chairs that should
circle the firepit
remain folded and frowning
sunscreen is not needed today
my straw sun hat waits
in the new red pop-up tent
my much-needed rain-hat
remains on the hook at home
no matter   our caring friendship
our conversation is cheerful
our smiles beam through the rain

Turn of the Chair

I sip my first morning cup of coffee
flavored with a touch of cinnamon
the warm mug soothes my hands
I decide to turn my favorite chair
usually it faces west toward Salish Sea
now instead of tireless tug boats
I look eastward to Bell's Family Farm
watch sheep wander up to the fence
as customers drive up to the farm stand
stocked with sweet strawberries in summer
fall filled with Yukon Gold potatoes
squash   beets   kale   lettuce   and   cut dahlias
the red stand remains unattended
leave your money or check in the box
at night a light turns on with any movement
which can be distracting as cars pass by
today a truck loaded with hay bales arrives
to provide feed for Black Angus cattle
they keep for The Three Sisters' Farm
grass grazing is next to nothing now
our dry summer turns the fields to brown
in spring it grows lush and green
the farmer brings a bundle for the sheep
they rush up to him knowing he offers food
I sit quietly and watch with a smile
warmed by a stream of sunlight
a round rainbow reflects on our wall
created from our stained-glass window
all this reward   by a simple turn of a chair

Our One Day Dog

It's Memorial Day; our son, his wife and our two granddaughters' ages 9 and 12 are returning from a weekend camp out. They also had a young boy, a family friend with them. This took place at Cornet Bay Learning Center where there are group camping facilities available by reservation. It is part of Deception Pass State Park. They are heading home, driving southbound on West Beach Road not far from Joseph Whidbey State Park. Running towards them in the middle of the road is a shaggy plump spotted brown and white dog. Cars are slowing down to avoid him and my son, with encouragement from the kids, stops to catch and rescue him. The dog was willing to get into the car and happy to receive a chicken nugget or two. He had a collar on, but there was no identification attached.

When they arrive at our house my daughter-in-law greets me with, "We brought you a dog and a temporary grandson."

I had been wanting a dog and given up on a grandson, so I replied, "That's great, what more could I want!"

I locate an old leash and the kids take him for a walk through the field. He must weigh about fifty pounds and they have named him Harry, since he shed profusely. On the walk they learn that he\is a she; so her name becomes Harriet. Upon returning they tie up Harriet to a post under our second story deck. She has water and shade, but when they climb up the stairs to the deck she starts to whimper. We were all sitting on the deck just above her and although we try to calm her, the whimpering increases. Our granddaughter's friend couldn't stand this and he started to cry. So Harriet was brought up on the deck to join us. Then, she appears to be happy, laps up more water, lots of attention and soon contentedly naps.

I call the Whidbey Animal Improvement Foundation phone number, but since it is a holiday, no one answers. I leave a message about this "Harriet" lost dog and give them a description.

All the while I'm secretly hoping that maybe, just possibly this is the dog that we've been seeking. One hears of stories where an abandoned dog actually finds a new family. We have been looking for a dog for over a year now. We had driven to Bellingham, Burlington, Silverdale, Seattle and of course Coupeville shelters. For numerous reasons, we had not yet located a good fit for our situation. Maybe this appealing mutt could become our forever friend.

Our son's family and friend had to leave as they had a ferry reservation to head home to Port Townsend. They bid goodbye to us and of course, sadly, to Harriet.

We go in the house with Harriet happily following and leaving a trail of white fur wherever she walked. Soon it was approaching dinner time for us and no doubt for Harriet dog. We had a container full of dog biscuits, but no actual dog food. I called our neighbor to see if we could borrow some. She was happy to give us some and added that she would come over, take a photo of the dog and put it on Facebook. Not long after that we get a phone call. It was not directly from the dog's owner, however; she appeared to know who the owner was. Within fifteen minutes we receive another call that turns out to be the true and very relieved owners.

Very soon after that they appear at our door immensely thankful, as they had been looking for her all day. She had never left their neighborhood cul-de-sac before, so they were truly puzzled as to what had happened. We learn her real name is "Micky." We also learn that perhaps the reason she was so mellow in our house is that she is partially deaf. We have a pleasant conversation with Micky's owners and as often happens on Whidbey Island it turns out that the lady owner had gone to a local high school with our neighbor that put the dog's photo on Facebook.

With a smile and a certain sadness, I bid goodbye to our "dog for a day" Micky alias Harriet.

.

Grandpa-Tree Trail

Grandpa-Tree trail is located in Fort Ebey
State Park

I walk the Grandpa-Tree Trail
urged onward by huge ancient trees
I don't know which
handsome tree is grandpa
I gaze upward in wonder
so much that I stumble
so quiet I can hear my breath
drops of rain remain
on the salal leaves
the forest smells fresh
it's vibrant green
washed clean from
this morning's rain
I stare at all these
handsome grandpas
some stand straight
some bend sideways
some lean on youthful trees
I wait and listen
for them to talk
I feel they have
something to tell me
the silence is intoxicating
yet I yearn for
Grandpa-Tree's message

The Path

Once open and welcoming
now cluttered and closing
heavy overhang of vines
reach out and rip at my heart
the start of something magical
now feels heavy and harmful
thorns and thistles lean outward
grow and grab my ankles
hammer on my emotions

I come upon Bear dog's grave
entrance blocked by broken branches
trail along the way to special place
suffers the same obstruction
winter winds whipped havoc
so many branches down

I stumble

cling tightly to my cane
then continue so slowly
the familiar path seems longer
an oak tree I planted struggles
its progress strangled by vines
I continue cautiously
only to find a fallen willow tree
blocking the usual clear path

carefully I crawl over
trying to avoid stinging nettles
many grown taller than me
I pass what was once a bench
now collapsed driftwood
resting flat on the ground
I hear a distant bird call
it sounds like *whoo whoo*
not an owl this time of day
it must be a mourning dove

I reach the center of the woods
once a glade now a shaded grove
the fire-pit filled with weeds
wooden benches and picnic table
trimmed pale green with moss
beneath the alders a bright
harsh green carpet of nettles

I continue the curving circle path
pale blue spring wild flowers smile at me
I come to the only bench still standing
its across from Rascal's resting place
how I wish I could hug my big hairy dog
he's long gone but I still see
his handsome happy face

farther along the overgrown path
stands a carved wooden eagle
I have named her Marvel
I talk to her

she listens

the circle path about complete
I come to a large and low leaning tree
we were each once strong
standing upright and straight
how long will it be

until one of us collapses

Bill Wilson

With roots in the southeast, Bill Wilson came to Whidbey Island in 1990 after a career in the U.S. Air Force. He has degrees in English and journalism as well as an MBA. On Whidbey Bill wrote numerous news and feature stories for several Whidbey Island newspapers and received awards from the Society of Professional Journalists and The Washington Newspaper Association. He later worked as a college English instructor and marketing writer for a scientific equipment company. With wife Myrna, he spends winters in Canada skiing Big White Mountain near Kelowna, B.C. where they both volunteer for the Royal Canadian Mounted Police and previously volunteered for the ski resort as Snow Hosts. Bill has published **Stowaway**, a literary sci-fi novella, along with **Offspring**, its novel-length sequel, as well as stories and poems in previous Whidbey Writers Group anthologies. Now retired from all but writing and the honey-do list, he remains a slave to the fickle muses and mountain snowfall.

Deceived

Note: An earlier version of this story appeared in Whidbey Connections, *a previous WWG anthology. We include it in this book as an apt lead-in to the story that follows…*

From the quarterdeck of the sloop *HMS Discovery*, Sailing Master Joseph Whidbey cocked his tricorne to shade his eyes from a bright morning sun, an unaccustomed sight in recent weeks. Whidbey welcomed the warmth of the sun this Thursday, June 7, AD 1792; but when the sun came, the wind died, or nearly so. Thus, the ship's sails luffed uselessly in the light and changing breeze while timbers creaked, and the ship bobbed like a toy boat in a washtub. To make matters worse, tidal current began sweeping *Discovery* and its tender, *HMS Chatham,* to the south – the reverse of the intended course.

Its progress thwarted, *Discovery* dropped anchor near a small sandy island which tailed away to the east into a narrow spit. To an eagle soaring above, the island might have resembled a long-handled spoon, if indeed eagles thought of such things. Once anchored, the two ships rested about two leagues west of a much larger, heavily forested land mass, apparently a peninsula connected to this region of North America's mainland.

Whidbey gazed beyond that near shore at the mountains to the east stretching north and south

farther than he could see. Most wore mottled patches
of melting snow, but two peaks stood high above the
others – each boasting a solid white blanket reaching
well down from its summit. The mountain to the
south was already named for Admiral Peter Rainer,
the *Discovery* captain's friend, and the other to the
north for Third Lieutenant Joseph Baker, who first
spotted the massive mountain.

Baker stood on the quarterdeck beside Whidbey
and the other ship's officers waiting for orders from
Captain George Vancouver. On the main deck
below, two seamen swabbed the sun-bleached
wooden planks near the treelike mainmast. Other
crewmen repaired sails, tightened rigging, and
worked at various other tasks. One man could be
observed sleeping in the sun atop a large coil of line
– apparently in no fear of retribution from the
officers above. These assembled officers also
included botanist, and now ship's surgeon,
Archibald Menzies, as well as Second Lieutenant
Peter Puget.

Puget too had been immortalized in geography,
his name given to the inland waterway their ships
lately plowed: Puget Sound. Naming landmarks
seemed to be the captain's favorite pastime,
Whidbey thought. He tried not to envy those so
honored, but he wondered what more he must do for
Vancouver to find his name a worthy moniker for a
point, a bay, or even a small hill. More than a dozen
years Whidbey had served under this man, following
him from ship to ship – *Discovery* being the third. *Is
this how he rewards such long-suffering loyalty?*

No less than Puget, Whidbey had endured

countless days and nights away from the ship, exploring every rock and tree, and greeting hundreds of curious natives along the shores of Mr. Puget's sound. Whidbey was especially irked that Vancouver had named an inlet on the west side of Saratoga Passage "Penn's Cove" for his "particular friend" – a friend no doubt spending his nights in a warm, dry English bed, likely accompanied by an even warmer specimen of feminine pulchritude.

Particular friend, my lily-white arse, Whidbey thought. *It was I who explored the cove, charted it, and became ambassador to scores of Indians, not to mention their packs of barking dogs, many having been shorn like sheep... The natives were courteous and generous, perhaps to a fault. But communicating proved tedious, involving much pointing and gesturing, not to mention the multitude of loud, mutually meaningless words. We did understand when they insisted we eat their fare, including some tasty smoked fish and not-so-tasty roasted roots of some kind that left one pining for a real potato.*

Even more disconcerting was their poking and prodding at our clothes and skin. I eventually realized they believed we had all painted our skins. Ultimately, I had to open my waistcoat and lift my shirt to convince him my skin was indeed white – curious indeed, since the chief proudly exhibited two hangers of obvious European origin. Surely he acquired these swords through trade with other tribes... This tribe also shows the marks of a far more ominous European product – smallpox – in their faces and in their graveyards.

Upon finally leaving that picturesque cove, with

Mr. Baker's Mountain looming in the north, I managed to run aground on one of "particular friend's" shoals. Thanks to a rising tide and half a dozen strong Indians, we finally broke free...

The captain's voice interrupted Whidbey's reverie.

Vancouver grimaced, then stifled a burp while rubbing his generous midsection. "I see no profit in delaying further surveys while waiting for fair wind to next anchor," said the captain.

Vancouver swept his left arm in an exaggerated gesture across the eastern horizon. "This unbroken chain of mountains makes it apparent we will not find the elusive Northwest Passage emerging from this section of New Albion coast; but our mission is to explore and survey, so explore and survey we shall.

"Mr. Whidbey, make ready the cutter with a week's provisions... Mr. Puget, do likewise with the launch. Proceed northeast to explore and chart inlets you encounter. *Discovery* and *Chatham* will proceed north to Strawberry Bay as soon as wind and tide permit. You'll rendezvous with us there."

"Aye, Captain," Whidbey and Puget replied in unison.

This waxes a bit tiresome, thought Whidbey. *Why doesn't he send Baker this time? My aching bones don't recover as fast as his young ones.*

"Should I attend this excursion, Captain?" Menzies asked. "The terrain appears more rugged than that we encountered to the south, likely giving rise to more unique plant specimens."

"Good God no," Vancouver replied. "Your

dammed hothouse is already overflowing onto my deck. This ship is beginning to more closely resemble a conservatory than the pride of King George's Navy... Besides, I fear I may need your services as medical officer."

Menzies nodded to the captain, then scribbled in his notebook as Whidbey and Puget headed below to make ready for their expedition.

After selecting his crew of seven able seamen and overseeing loading of provisions, Whidbey followed his crew down the brine-soaked cargo net into the 22-foot cutter. There he took his place in the bow. His crew consisted of veterans of his excursion to the eastern shore of the nearby peninsula, so he felt confident in their skills and diplomacy with the Indians. The crew manned the oars since almost no wind pushed on the gaff-rigged mainsail. Both of the vessels' foresails remained furled.

As the boat sliced through the glassy water to the rhythm of the oars, Whidbey took in the scene to the south. The sight of the Olympic Mountains rising like silent sentinels above a dissipating fog bank brought to mind the voyage east from the Pacific Ocean more than a month before – along the strait named for Juan de Fuca, a Greek explorer sailing under the Spanish flag some two centuries prior. Or so the story went. Captain Vancouver had expressed doubts, saying the only accounts of de Fuca's voyage came by word of mouth. Regardless of who arrived first, the sight of such a place made Whidbey almost forget his disdain for this latest excursion and his life aboard a cramped vessel for the previous two years. Never mind it would likely be two years hence before he would again set foot on English soil. He could not think of more pleasant environs should they become marooned, thinking especially of the shores along Mr. Penn's Cove, whoever he may be. Unworthy name notwithstanding, Whidbey found the land bordering the cove pleasant and varied, featuring dales and meadows with wildflowers and shrubbery interspersed throughout the lush forest – in his mind rivaling the most manicured estates of England.

"Get us past the next point before the end of first dogwatch and you all get extra ration of grog," Whidbey shouted.

"Suppose that means spruce beer. Right, Mr. Whidbey?" Walter Dillon, the coxswain asked in a snickering Irish brogue.

"Indeed...unless one of you has a key to the captain's whiskey cabinet," Whidbey replied with a hearty laugh.

Despite being promised nothing but their already allotted grog ration, the other six seamen rowed hard, moving the boat smartly northward along the shore as a curious sea otter swam alongside, repeatedly rolling front to back while several gulls hovered and squawked from above, no doubt looking for a handout. The shore loomed larger and larger off the starboard beam, revealing alternating stretches of beach gently rising toward lush forests and sheer brown cliffs looking as if a careless mason had left before finishing his work.

Like balm for aching muscles, a fair

northwesterly breeze finally began to raise ripples across the water, allowing the crew to hoist sail and remain on a steady reach at about four knots. Then still in calm water, Puget's boat fell nearly half a league behind the cutter's wake.

As Whidbey's cutter neared the intended inlet, a sudden rush of flood tide current propelled it headlong between the southern point of the inlet mouth and a small island about half a mile further north.

"Great God in Heaven! Where be all this water headed?" Whidbey shouted over the onrushing current. "Hold fast the tiller, Dillon. Furl the sails, stow the oars, and hold on, men! Too late to warn Puget!"

"Looks like another island dead ahead," Dillon yelled as he pointed. "The current splits around it, Mr. Whidbey,"

"Take the right channel. It appears wider," said Whidbey, still straining his voice over the rushing tide. "And keep us in the center. Don't think we want to challenge those bloody rocks."

"Aye, aye, sir," Dillon responded. He leaned his shoulder into the hardwood tiller, and the craft responded with a lurch to starboard and across the churning current.

Despite Dillon's best efforts to hold a steady course, the boat veered sharply back to port when it passed through a sudden whirlpool. After spinning out of the vortex, the vessel moved wildly toward the rocky island. And before Dillon could regain control, the boat scraped the branch of an evergreen growing almost horizontally from the side of a sheer cliff that plunged directly into the roiling water. "Bloody hell!" one of the oarsmen screamed in pain and fright as he and his portside mates ducked to avoid being impaled on the tree.

Just before the craft plunged headlong into the rocky cliff, Dillon managed to steer it back toward the center of the channel.

As the boat finally slowed into relatively calmer water, a huge black raven soared overhead and cawed his critique of the spectacle below. The crew broke into spontaneous cheers.

Whidbey pulled a handkerchief from the pocket of his waistcoat and wiped the salt spray from his face. "Nice work, Dillon...

"Gents, it appears we have been deceived. This," he said, pointing to the rising shore to the south, "is not a peninsula, but an island."

"Yes, sir, Mr. Whidbey," said Dillon. "Your island, I'd say."

"I doubt that," replied Whidbey. "Surely the captain has another 'particular friend' he has promised a spot on the map."

Whidbey looked back at the pass they'd just traversed and watched Puget's launch rounding the point into the pass. While waiting for the other boat, Whidbey looked up at the bluffs on each side – bluffs reaching several hundred feet above the inland sea. Then low in the sky, the sun cast long shadows across land and water.

"I'd hate to be the engineer in charge of building a bridge across that," said Whidbey.

"A bridge? You really think anyone would ever try it, Mr. Whidbey?" asks Dillon.

"Of course. We English can do anything..."

Author's Note: And maybe it happened something like that... If Joseph Whidbey kept a journal, it unfortunately did not survive. So we can only guess at details beyond existing documents, primarily the logs of George Vancouver. (Walter Dillon, a 27-year-old Irishman, was indeed listed on the Discovery *manifest as an able-bodied seaman, but he may or may not have been the coxswain on the ship's cutter as it negotiated the treacherous pass.)*

Perhaps to Whidbey's surprise, Vancouver did of course name the long, meandering island "Whidbey's Island," and the channel between Whidbey and Fidalgo islands "Deception Pass." The bridge over Deception Pass opened some 143 years later in 1935, having taken ten years for the Americans (who can also do anything) to complete.

Discovery returned to England in 1795 to little fanfare. Vancouver received almost no credit during his lifetime for his voyage of discovery. In fact, he was attacked by his political enemies for a number of perceived transgressions and even challenged to a duel by Thomas Pitt, a well-connected midshipman he had disciplined and sent home in disgrace. Even his loyal sailing master, Joseph Whidbey, disputed Vancouver's claim for extra pay as expedition astronomer – duties Whidbey insisted he performed.

Vancouver died in obscurity in 1798 at age 40 of an unknown illness, possibly Addison's disease, which affects the adrenal gland. His brother John Vancouver eventually published George's extensive and comprehensive logs. Long after his death, the importance of his voyage began to be acknowledged. Today Vancouver is the namesake for the largest island along North America's west coast and the largest city in British Columbia, Canada, as well as Vancouver, Washington, in the U.S.

Joseph Whidbey left the Royal Navy in 1799 and went on to a distinguished career as a marine engineer. His most notable project was the massive Plymouth Breakwater, still standing near the entrance to the English Channel.

Deceived Again

Feathers. Like snowflakes caught in an updraft, hundreds of them drifted down onto the hood and adorned the front seat of Neil Dortson's sky-blue Beamer convertible. Dead stopped on the south span of Deception Pass Bridge heading off Whidbey Island, Neil could see only the back end of an open semi piled high with chicken crates. He couldn't decide which smelled worse: diesel exhaust or chicken shit.

Minutes before, the truck had stopped suddenly, air brakes squealing. The driver must not have noticed the construction flagger's sign soon enough. Whatever the reason, crates shifted and banged into each other. Chickens clucked and clawed. Results: feathers ruffled, literally.

Neil started to reach for the ragtop control, but stopped. "No use closing it now," he muttered to himself. "Just have to hope all these feathers blow out once I get moving again."

Wonder how long this'll take, he thought. Seemed to him like more and more traffic jams on and off this island. *This damn bridge can be such a pain in the ass. I know it's over 80 years old, but couldn't they work on it in the middle of the night?*

His 86-year-old Aunt Katherine – and don't call her Kate – expected him to pick her up in Anacortes for an appointment to update her will. He reached for his cell phone. "Call Aunt K… Hello, Auntie. This is Neil…What?... Neil, your nephew, Neil. Sorry. The cell reception is lousy here. Traffic stopped on the bridge, so might be late… Right, I'll do my best, but you may want to let the lawyer know what's happening… I hope so. See you soon."

The old biddy will probably disinherit me if I'm not on time, he thought, *if she ever "inherited" me in the first place. Who cares? Don't need her money anyway.* A recent computer science graduate from the University of Washington, Neil already earned six figures from Microsoft and was allowed to telecommute four days a week from his home in Oak Harbor.

At least it was a nice day, chicken feathers notwithstanding. Only a few wispy clouds dotted the bright blue sky. Well below the bridge, the mid-morning sun glanced off minute ripples across the pass water below. Neil reasoned it must have been at or near slack tide. Gently floating feathers bore witness to the lack of wind. Surrounded and stifled by technology, he wondered what island namesake Joseph Whidbey faced in the late 1700's when his oar-and-sail-powered launch first navigated the treacherous current below – no doubt more serious challenges than poor cell service.

Splat. A white blob drooled like spilled Alfredo sauce over the oyster-colored leather passenger side headrest. That ruined the reverie.

"Shit. That's not going to blow out… At least the S.O.B. missed my head." He shook his fist at the still-hovering gull. He then regretted heading out with the top down, but on such a beautiful Indian summer day, maybe the last top-down day till spring… And who knew he'd be sitting still long enough to present such a tempting avian target.

With a still-wary eye for more bombing bird sorties, Neil noticed a teenage girl on the bridge walkway attempting a selfie against the rail. *Far enough!* He wanted to yell to her. At least that 180-foot fall would give her time enough to see her short life flash before her eyes. No telling how long to recover her crab-eaten body.

Before the gruesome scenario could unfold, selfie girl's boyfriend managed to pull his crab-bait girlfriend away from the railing and avert a morbid headline. So then Neil looked past the couple, across the water and east toward Strawberry Island, Hoypus Point, and beyond, where the pass widened into Skagit Bay. Thus reminded that he lived in a special place, he found it all too easy to become jaded as more and more traffic traveled the bridge and jammed island roads. He couldn't blame people for wanting to live here, but he sometimes wondered how more idyllic the island would have remained had the bridge never been built.

"Just thank the Lord above you have a bridge to cross," he remembered Aunt Katherine saying. "I recall when you might wait hours for the ferry from Hoypus Point." *Doubt you really remember that, Auntie,* he thought. *If you're eighty-six, that means you'd have been three when the bridge opened in 1935. Besides, that ferry wait might be worth not having all this traffic. Thank God there's no bridge at the other end of this island.*

While the last of the line of cars coming from Fidalgo Island passed him in the opposite lane, and Neil waited for the unseen flagger to give his lane the go ahead, a massive fog bank rolled up the pass from the Strait of Juan de Fuca and obscured everything, even the chicken truck just feet ahead…

Almost as suddenly, the fog cleared to an odd, piercing sound: *a oo ga, a oo ga.*

"Say what?" Neil asked himself out loud. He craned his neck and saw a shiny black Model T Ford – or maybe Model A – behind him making the unearthly sound while venting steam from under its hood. Looked like one he saw in the LeMay car museum in Tacoma. So he shook his head and rubbed his eyes, but the bizarre scene persisted.

"Pull ahead already," the driver shouted from his open window. "The boat's finished unloading. You think that fancy Packard makes you special?"

"What? Packard?"

That's when Neil gazed about his vehicle interior and realized he no longer sat in his 2018 BMW. Again, he could see an almost clear sky above, so he still sat in a convertible. But his instrument panel consisted of a cluster of round analog gauges and a few switches framed in a silver-looking trim, all mounted in a polished woodgrain dashboard. His leather-padded steering wheel had morphed into smooth varnished wood. To his right, a long black metal rod, mounted to the floor and topped with a polished wooden knob to match the steering wheel, had replaced his Beamer's console-mounted shifter. The only thing that hadn't changed: dozens of white feathers coating the passenger seat and floorboard.

Ahead, the traffic jam on Deception Pass Bridge had given way to a ferry line along a narrow gravel road winding beneath and between massive fir and cedar trees. When he looked up through the almost flat windshield, he saw a woman frantically beckoning from the wood-planked open deck of a small ferry boat. The sign on the pilot house read: DECEPTION PASS FERRY.

"Get moving, fancy pants," she said in a Scandinavian-sounding accent. "I got a schedule to keep."

"Great," he said aloud to himself, still wondering what happened and if he'd lapsed into some kind of lucid daydream back on the bridge in 2018. Whatever happened included replacing his faded jeans and Seattle Mariners tee shirt with "fancy pants" of a dark gray shiny material plus a navy double-breasted blazer with polished brass buttons.

Hands on hips, the woman on the boat intensified her frown.

"Quick, how do I drive this thing, and where's the seat belt?" he asked no one.

Spurred by the agitated ferry attendant and some primal instinct, Neil reached for the starter button, and the powerful Packard engine roared to life then belched smoke at the Model A behind. Without ever having driven a straight shift, he eased off on the clutch and pulled up the ramp onto the small ferry's starboard side behind yet another chicken truck; but this one was just an old rusty pickup with a dozen or so chickens, all in one cage.

Thank God. Would hate to think those twenty-first-century chickens followed me back in time.

Just four more cars – really old cars – pulled in behind him. Looked to be another six on the port side. *A twelve-car ferry? That should spur 2018 commerce.*

Of course this can't be happening, but might as well try to blend in till I wake up.

The woman who waved him onto the ferry walked up and held out her hand. She wore a dark blue peacoat and a white officer-style hat with blondish hair spilling below the brim. Still confused, Neil reached for the power window control which didn't seem to exist. Once he noticed the window crank on the door, he remembered his ragtop and windows were already down.

"Yes, ma'am?"

"Fifty cents, please. No free rides on my boat."

"Uh, okay." He looked for coins in the glove box and found none, so he fished in his pants pocket and pulled out a handful of change where he spotted a half dollar bearing the image of an Ancient-Greek-looking woman wearing a long, flowing dress and holding a sheaf of wheat. "Here you go," he said, handing her the coin. *Glad my Dreamweaver supplied all the props.*

She then walked away, apparently to collect from the other drivers.

A whistle shrieked as the ferry pulled away from the dock. Neil got out and stood beside the classic blue Packard, complete with deployed rumble seat. He wondered why, since he was the only passenger. *Maybe my 1930's doppelganger just dropped off a carload.*

Looking west he could barely discern the outline of the bridge, which must have been at least a mile away. So how did he end up on this little ferry so far from the bridge, and why would a ferry even be here?

The deck lady walked up again. The top of her hat barely reached Neil's chin.

"Haven't seen you and your fancy car come across before. It looks like you survived the market crash just fine... I'm Berte Olson. I own this ferry, but had to work the deck today since Marv called in sick. That's my husband, Augie, in the pilothouse... So, what brings you up our way?"

"Going to Anacortes to visit my aunt," he said. *Berte Olson, hmm. Where have I heard that name? Oh, yeah. There was a musical about her life a few years back at the park amphitheater.*

"Coming from where?" she pressed.

He paused. *Can't say Oak Harbor*, he thought. *She probably knows everybody there.*

"Uh... Everett."

"Must not be in a much of a hurry."

"True," he responded. "Wanted to see Whidbey Island and especially the pass... What are they doing to the bridge?"

"Building it, unfortunately," she answered with a scowl. "Don't you read the papers?"

Neil strained his eyes looking toward the bridge, which looked to be all there. *Must be nearing completion.*

"George Morse tried for years, rest his soul," Berte continued, "but it took that sweet-talking Pearl Wanamaker to push it through the statehouse. Lyle Muzzall and his fund-raising picnics at Cranberry Lake did not help me any either. I'll be out of business next summer. Summer of '35, that'll be a bleak season."

"Sorry to hear that. I have a feeling you'll do just fine though."

"I hope you are right."

Neil remembered reading that Norwegian immigrant Berte Olson had fought long and hard to scuttle the bridge project. Despite ultimately losing the battle, she succeeded with other ferry routes – a real pioneer woman.

Her most prominent opponent, Pearl Wanamaker, pushed for the bridge while a representative in the state legislature. Wanamaker later saw it finished and cut the ribbon at the dedication. A road on the island also bears her name, he recalled.

And George Morse, a sea captain who settled in Oak Harbor, became the first aggressive advocate for a bridge across Deception Pass. But he died before his dream became reality.

"Better get back in," Berte said, looking askance at Neil. "About to land." She moved just ahead of the Packard to the bow and picked up a coil of thick woven line while the evergreen-covered hills of south Fidalgo Island filled the view ahead.

As Neil waited for Berte's signal to pull off the boat, another fog materialized, and he soon heard a more familiar horn blaring.

"Move it, asshole, before they stop us again," a driver yelled from behind.

Neil opened his eyes to no more fog and found himself again in bright sunshine on the south span of the bridge. Still trailing feathers, the chicken truck had already pulled slowly ahead a hundred feet or so onto Pass Island. Neil followed and nodded to the flagger lady moving an orange SLOW sign left and right. He glanced at the clock on this Beamer's dashboard.

"Only five minutes from 2018 to 1934 and back," he said to himself. "Guess I'll get Auntie to her appointment on time after all. Thank you, Pearl Wanamaker, Lyle Muzzall, George Morse, and even you, Berte Olson."

Deception Pass Bridge

Heather Parsley

Heather arrived on beautiful Whidbey Island 18 years ago. She taught Special Education for 15 years on her native Oregon Coast and for 5 years on Whidbey, as well as working for the Navy Child Development Center. Her greatest joy came from working as a docent volunteer at Admiralty Head Lighthouse.

Heather's first published work is an article, "Camping With Your Cat," in an e-magazine, Outdoors Northwest, where her cat Harliquinn was the cover girl. Writing a memoir about her dad's life is her current project. Both Heather and her husband, Dennis, are happily retired. They spend their days traveling, motorcycling, and camping across the U.S. with their adventure cats, Ziva and Harliquinn.

Treasure Hunt

Ivan felt in his pocket and ran his fingers over the object to make sure it was still there. He looked at his watch: 10:13. She was supposed to meet him here at 10:00. *Did she get up late? Did she get into an accident on the way to Cornet Bay?* Checking his messages on his phone he found none from her.

Ivan looked out across the bay at the wisps of fog creeping across the calm blue water. He could see part of Ben Ure Island peeking out from the gray mist, the tops of the trees lit with fiery sunrays trying to chase away the fog. *Someday, I'll rent the cabin on the island and wake up snuggled next to her.* The few boats in the Cornet Bay Marina bobbed in unison as a small fishing boat left the dock. Ivan checked his watch again: 10:24. *Where is she? It isn't like her to be so late.* Anxiously he stepped back and forth wishing she'd show up soon, especially on this day.

He saw a car coming down the road, a Ford Mustang. *Dang, not her.* A purple Ford pickup with a canopy wheeled around the corner. Julia pulled up and parked next to his white truck. "You finally made it," Ivan stated tersely.

"Yeah, there was an accident on Highway 20 that had every car backed up."

"You couldn't text me you'd be late?" Ivan said with a scowl.

"By the time I noticed the time, I was already

here." She shrugged.

Seeing her frown and remembering his true reason for this hike, he wrapped her in a hug. "You ready for this adventure?"

Julia replied, "Sure, just let me get my water bottle."

Ivan, a seasoned geocacher with the code name "Wanderingman," had introduced the sport to Julia when they met two years ago. He loved the thrill of finding the hidden ammo boxes or the tiny mini-containers by just using GPS coordinates and navigation skills to locate caches. It is a treasure hunt for grownups, and children too, that has grown into a worldwide activity. *I'm so glad I've already found my treasure.* Pulling out his GPS finder he put in the coordinates for today's cache.

"All set to hike to 'Nary a ferry now' at the end of this trail?" Ivan motioned towards the start.

Julia started walking ahead of him all bundled up in a down coat and knit hat. Ivan could see Julia's breath visible in the crisp air as she strode up the trail. All was quiet except for a few birds singing and her boots crunching fallen leaves. "Can you smell the fir trees mixed with that salt air? I love living on this Island." Ivan beamed as he took in a deep breath.

"It is especially beautiful here with the morning light playing on the water," Julia agreed.

He enjoyed going on adventures with Julia. Her

infectious energy had drawn him in as soon as they met. A simple girl, with long auburn hair, brown eyes, and a round face with a mouth that was either smiling or cracking a joke. At thirty-six, near his age, she lived her life to the fullest. He really didn't know what she saw in him, with his light brown hair, hazel eyes, and tall stature. He didn't see himself as handsome, as his friends teased him that he was too clean cut, and a bit of a geek. He touched the smooth object in his pocket again. *Yup, still there.*

"This geocache has some local history attached to it," stated Ivan.

"Yeah, what kind of history?" asked Julia.

Walking up close beside her he explained, "Before the building of the Deception Pass Bridge, one way onto Whidbey Island was by ferry. We're going to the old ferry dock at the end of Hoypus Point." Becoming more animated, he continued, "A woman named Berte Olson was the first woman to pilot a ferry in Washington. She ran the *Deception Pass*, a boat that held twelve Model-Ts, then the *Acorn,* which held sixteen cars. It ran between Hoypus Point on Whidbey and Dewey's Landing across the water on Fidalgo Island."

"Wow, I wonder what the ferry line was like in those days? I still get impatient waiting in those long ferry lines just to get off the island," complained Julia.

"No lines." He chuckled. "If you wanted to ride the ferry, you would hit an old lumberjack saw with a mallet to bring the boat over to your side." Ivan remembered his dad telling him these stories.

***

The sun started to warm up the trail as the golden and burnt brown leaves sparkled from the dew left from the earlier fog. Branches made a fairy tunnel as they walked through the passage. Julia stopped often to capture images of the colorful trees, and some of Ivan, with her phone.

"Oh, you can see the bridge from here," she exclaimed as she walked to an opening in the trees and saw the Deception Pass Bridge illuminated in the sunlight.

Ivan explained, "That bridge was the end of the ferry for Berte. This short, stout woman drove down to Olympia a few times and marched into the Governor's Office. Berte was determined to have the Governor veto the bridge-building bill."

"But the bridge is here. She didn't succeed," said Julia.

"Berte's tenacity helped some, as she stopped the building for six years so her ferry could continue." Ivan motioned to the bridge. "When the bridge was finally opened in 1935, her little ferry went out of business, so she left Fidalgo Island. Later, she bought the franchise for the Port Gamble-Shine Ferry in Hood Canal and continued to pilot her boats."

"That's sad that the little ferry stopped. I would have liked to meet Berte. She sounds like a fierce woman," noted Julia.

"I think you would have liked her. Women had to be strong to live on these rugged islands back in those days," declared Ivan. *Like the strength I see in you,* he thought as he squeezed her hand briefly then walked back to the trail.

Julia snapped a few more pictures of the cobalt and turquoise water swirling in rough currents to the bridge. "I can barely make out people standing on the walkway, but I see a powerboat splashing up white spray." She beamed.

"Let's keep moving. We still have more to go," declared Ivan. He was breathing in the salty air as Julia started walking back to the trail. Standing on the trail in the sunlight, he saw her frame a picture of him. Ivan watched Julia's foot catch on a branch as she stepped toward him. Ivan lunged to catch her fall, but his rescue was too slow.

Helplessly, he watched her tumble down, her outstretched hands striking the wet leaves. Her phone flew out of her hand and bounced as it hit the ground.

As Ivan reached her, he bent down to help her up, asking frantically, "Julia, are you hurt?"

Leaves covered her hands and pants. Brushing off the leaves, she took a deep breath, and while rubbing her hands stated, "I think I'm okay. No blood, oh…"

Ivan noticed her dirty hand had a red streak across her palm. "You're bleeding." Dropping his backpack, he dug out a blue handkerchief and a water bottle. He poured some water over her palm and gently cleaned out her wound with the handkerchief. The cut stopped bleeding, and in all the commotion Ivan almost forgot about the reason for this hike. Holding her shaking hand is his, he looked up into her wide eyes and a flush came over his cheeks.

Ivan dropped her hand quickly, and asked, "Do you think you can make it to the point, or do you want to go back to the trucks?" Dreading the answer, he waited with his breath held.

"I think I can make it. It's farther back to the trucks than it is to the end. We're almost there now."

Visibly exhaling, he took her hand again and pulled her up. "You better stay with me, little girl, I'll protect you from the big bad roots," he teased to put her at ease.

As they arrived at Hoypus Point, Ivan could see a small sandy beach surrounded by rockwork and driftwood. Julia was busy taking pictures again, now of the wood and pilings of the old ferry landing, as Ivan checked his GPS while he searched for the geocache box.

Moving some rocks, he quickly located the box and looked to see where Julia was standing. Waiting for her to look away he reached into his right pocket to pull out the ring he would place in the box.

He felt around in his pocket only to feel empty cloth. *Did I drop it on the way here? Did it fall out when I was helping Julia?* In a panic, he checked his pocket again with no joy, then quickly checked his left pocket. At last, with a sigh of relief, he felt the ring in his left pocket, then looked at it in his hand. It looked silver, but it was a white gold ring with a single small diamond in a simple setting.

Gingerly placing it in the box, he closed it and yelled, "I think I found the cache."

Julia looked up and walked over to Ivan. His heart was beating so much faster, and he was sweating even in the cool air. Ivan held out the metal box to her and said, "I found it; here, you open it. Did you bring something to exchange in the box, as I asked?"

"Oh, yes, I have it in my pocket," she exclaimed as she pulled out a clear quartz crystal. Julia gave Ivan the crystal as she opened the box. Inside were some small toys, a pen with a rubber animal top, a logbook, and a ring. Taking out the logbook and the pen she began to record their geocache find with their code names, listing hers first as "Trekingpole," then Ivan's name as "Wanderingman." Looking up she asked, "What's the date today?"

Ivan was trembling and didn't hear a word Julia was saying. *Why doesn't she see the ring yet? Is she blind?*

"Ivan, are you all right? What's wrong?" Julia wondered.

"Are you sure that is *all* that's in the box? Look again," he stammered. Ivan clenched his fists at his sides as Julia rummaged through the box again. Then, suddenly, she stopped.

"Look at this. Someone put an old ring in the box. Isn't that cool?" Julia remarked as she held it up to Ivan.

Ivan took the ring from her in his trembling hand, got down on one knee, and held the ring out to his treasure.

"This was my Great-Grandma Berte's wedding

ring that was passed down to me. She was the
ferry captain here on this beach in 1924. I would
be honored if you would join our family as my
wife."

Berte Olson

Photo Courtesy of
Whidbey Island Historical Museum

Mike McNeff

Mike is a retired cop and lawyer who always wanted to write novels. So, when he retired that's just what he started doing. Since then, he has written four novels. His novels draw from his law enforcement experiences, which included working as a detective and on SWAT teams, and training with Special Forces. The novels also reflect his obsession with history and current events.

He has a beautiful wife, four great children, and seven wonderful grandchildren. In addition to writing, he does volunteer work and spends time teaching folks about firearms and shooting. He spends as much time as he can enjoying the outdoors of the Great Northwest.

The Christmas Flash

Deputy Sheriff Paul Mays poured a glass of wine for himself and one for his wife, Julie. The kids were in bed and it was time to wrap the presents and get them under the tree. Paul had worked every Christmas Eve for the last five years, but not this Christmas Eve; and Paul was savoring every moment.

He walked into the living room. The fireplace crackled warmth into the room in concert with the happiness radiated by the brightly decorated Christmas tree. Paul handed Julie her wine and kissed her. They touched glasses... The ringing phone shattered the moment.

"Don't answer it," Julie pleaded.

Paul took a deep breath and looked into his wife's pretty aquamarine eyes. "You know I have to." He walked to the phone and picked up the receiver.

"Paul Mays."

"Paul, it's Marie in dispatch. I hate to do this, but we have a missing child."

"Whereabouts?"

"Jack Early has the family at mile marker 25.5 on SR 20."

"Okay, I'll be there in twenty minutes."

Julie came up to him and put her arms around him. "Sometimes, I hate your job."

Paul pulled in behind other police cars parked along the highway. Snowflakes were falling lazily out of the sky. Sgt. Mark Long walked up to him.

"Hi, Paul. Sorry to ruin your Christmas Eve."

"No problem. What's the situation?"

"The family was driving through Whidbey from Portland on their way to Bellingham. Apparently, the missing boy and his father got into an argument. The father pulled over to deal with the kid, and the boy just took off."

"Which way did he go?"

"South. He ran into the forest toward Fort Ebey. This happened about two hours ago."

"That's not good. He's probably freezing."

"Yeah, that's why we've called out the extra troops. He's supposed to be a fast runner, likes to race, and his mother says he'll probably run if he sees a cop."

"Okay, Sarge, what's the real scoop?"

"The real scoop is the father is a complete jerk. The wife and the other kids in the car are terrified of him."

"Do we suspect abuse?"

"Instinct says yes, but we're not getting anything from the family. We can barely get a word out of them."

"Where do you want me?"

"You know, Paul, we have the forest pretty well covered about midway to the park now. In case this kid is the runner his mother says he is, why don't you head on down to the park and see what you can find."

"Okay. What's the boy's name?"

"His name is Samuel. He's about four feet, eight inches tall; ninety pounds; sandy-colored, collar-length hair. He's ten years old."

"How was he dressed?"

"He's wearing a light brown jacket, a green tee shirt, blue jeans, and running shoes. Oh, and he likes to be called Flash."

Paul laughed. "Sounds like the boy is a character. I'll let you know if I find anything. Oh, is he right-handed or left?"

"He's right-handed."

As he drove to the park, Paul started thinking about what a ten-year-old runaway would be looking for in this situation. The fort had several areas that were attractive to kids in the daytime, but it would be scary at night, like the ammunition bunker with its big concrete walls and metal doors. But it would be pitch black in there. Even with a flashlight it was a spooky place.

The main attraction for kids was always the beach, even at night. Paul had an idea where he would start his search. He approached the gate to the park, and Dave Sims, the resident park ranger, was there. Paul rolled down his window.

"Hi, Dave. Are you my welcoming committee?"

"You know you're always welcome here, Paul. Especially on Christmas Eve, at this time of night."

Paul laughed. "Sure, Dave. Whatever you say."

"Mark called me and said you were coming. Want me to come with you?"

"Naw. Enjoy your Christmas Eve. I have a plan to find this slippery suspect." Paul held up an infrared scope. "If he's here, this little gadget should easily see his heat signature in this weather."

"If you can sort him out from the wildlife."

"I've used this enough on burglars to know the difference now."

"Where do you think he might be?"

"Point Partridge area. If I don't see anything there, I'll work my way over to the main park and the campgrounds."

"If you come back this way, pick me up."

"Will do, Dave."

Paul went through the gate and turned right at the T-intersection. His search and rescue training taught him when lost people come to a fork in a road or path, they'll usually go in the direction of their strong side on flat ground. He started down to Point Partridge and turned off his headlights. He knew the road well and he navigated it slowly while using his scope to look for a heat signature. He noticed footprints in the thin covering of snow coming out of a forest trail onto the road. As he neared the parking area at the Point, he spotted what looked like the boy moving toward the beach. Paul stopped and turned off his car. He got out, went to the trunk, and retrieved his search and rescue backpack, which contained three days of supplies and equipment. He keyed his portable radio.

"U18, dispatch."

"U18."

"I've spotted the boy at Point Partridge. Have the other units set up a perimeter around the Point, but not enter. I'm going to see if I can get him to come to me. I'll be off the air for a bit."

"U18, understood."

Paul walked quietly down the beach trail, picking up firewood along the way. He used his flashlight now, following the boy's footprints. He made his way out to the beach and saw the prints went toward an eroded area of the bluff bordering the beach that formed a shallow cave. Paul stopped near the cave, but not too close.

He dug a small pit and put kindling at the bottom. Then laid layers of increasing sizes of wood on top of the kindling. He lit the fire with a lighter. The kindling caught, causing smoke first, then a small flame. Paul gently blew on the flame, causing it to spread.

As the flames grew, dancing shadows appeared on the bluff that allowed Paul to see the outline of the boy now and again. He put his hands over the fire and rubbed them.

"Ah, that feels good," he said out loud.

The outline of the boy seemed to be edging to the fire. Paul pulled out a large steel cup from his pack, poured water in it, and put it on the fire. The boy kept edging closer.

"You know, you'll get warmer a lot faster if you come closer to the fire," Paul called out to him.

"I don't want to get arrested."

The boy's voice told Paul the boy was frightened and shivering.

"Are you a criminal?"

The boy didn't answer right away. Then he said, "I don't think so."

"Well, Flash, then I'm not going to arrest you. Besides, it's Christmas Eve and I don't want to arrest anyone on Christmas Eve. In fact, I'm fixing us a Christmas Eve snack. Come join me."

The boy came slowly to the fire, and he was visibly shivering. Paul stood, took off this coat, and wrapped it around the boy.

"Go ahead and sit on the log where I was, Flash."

Paul reached into his pack, pulled out a space blanket, and wrapped it around himself. He also pulled out a package of freeze-dried beef stroganoff and poured the hot water from the cup into the package. He set the package down and handed Flash a fork.

"It'll be ready to eat in a couple of minutes." He looked at the boy. "So, I hear you like to be called Flash."

The boy nodded his head.

"Your mom says you're a really fast runner and I believe it. You have to be a very fast runner to run all the way here from the highway. How did you see in dark?"

A slight smile crossed the boy's lips. "I see pretty good at night, and the trail was a big one."

Paul pulled out his Swiss Army knife and began to feather a stick for more kindling. The boy's eyes zeroed in on the knife like a laser. "So, Flash, what made you decide to take this little jaunt?"

The boy pulled his knees close to him, wrapping Paul's jacket tight around his shoulders, and looked at the ground.

"It's all right if you don't want to talk about it." Paul opened the food package and took a taste. "Ah, gourmet cooking at its best. Here, Flash, eat up. But be careful; it's hot."

The boy took the package and started eating gingerly at first. After a few bites, he really started eating. *The kid is starved.* Paul continued making kindling, and Flash continued to watch the knife as he ate. The shivering subsided.

The snow stopped and Paul looked up at the sky. Breaks in the clouds were forming, revealing patches of the night sky thick with stars. Waves from the Salish Sea murmured onto the beach "You know what the favorite part of my job is, Flash?"

The boy shook his head.

"Helping folks who are having a rough time. That's the favorite part of my job. The thing is, I can't help somebody unless they tell me what's troubling them, because I'm not a mind reader. I've tried it a couple of times, but never could get the hang of it. How 'bout you? Are you a mind reader?"

The boy's eyes left the knife and looked into Paul's eyes as if searching for something. Paul let him look for as long as he wanted. The boy's eyes fell back to the knife.

"You want to do me a favor, Flash? I want to make some hot chocolate. Can you keep on making these kindling sticks for me?"

Flash's eyes lit up. "Yes."

"Do you know how to open and close a knife?"

The boy shrugged.

Paul showed him the blade. "This is the sharp edge here. You can tell because it's thinner than the other edge. See this groove here?"

"Yes."

"When the knife is closed, that's what you grab to open the knife. When you close it, you hold it in your left hand like this." Paul held the knife out. "Then you use the palm of your right hand to close it like this." Paul pressed his palm against the dull side of the blade and closed the knife. "That way you won't cut yourself. Here, you try it."

Flash took the knife and held it close to see the groove. Then he put his thumb and forefinger in it and pulled it open with a grunt. "That was hard."

"Maybe, but you did it. The more you do it, the easier it gets. Now close it."

The boy closed it as Paul had showed him. He looked up at Paul and smiled.

Paul handed him a stick. "Let's see you whittle."

"What's whittle?"

"Using a knife to make things out of wood. You saw how I was doing it. Just try to do the same thing."

Flash held the stick out and tried a cut. The knife just slipped off.

"Okay, we need to understand two things. One, you need to angle the blade to get it to bite." Flash tried it again. "Yes, like that, very good. The second thing is you want to hold it down and pointing out between your legs. Yes, good, except spread your legs wider so you don't stab them. There ya go. I think you got it."

The boy was grinning now as he worked on the stick. Paul turned the volume up on his radio and keyed the mic.

"U18, dispatch."

"U18."

"Contact made. We'll be at the office in a bit."

"U18, understood."

Paul put the radio back in its holder and reached into his bag and pulled out a package of hot chocolate. He poured more water in the cup and put it back on the fire.

"Are you taking me back now?"

"You in a hurry to get back?"

"No."

"Me neither. I'm enjoying the company. Besides, we haven't had our hot chocolate yet."

The boy smiled and went back to whittling. After a couple of minutes he asked, "What's your name?"

"You know, I did forget to introduce myself. I'm sorry. You can call me Paul."

The boy nodded as he whittled. "What's *your* dad like, Paul?"

"He was a good dad. Sometimes he would have to go away for a long time because he was a soldier and that was hard, but he was a good dad."

"Did he ever hit you?"

"He smacked me on my butt a couple times, because I did something bad."

"Did he ever punch you?"

Paul looked at Flash. "No, he never punched me."

"Did he ever knock you down?"

"No, he never knocked me down. Did your dad do that to you?"

Flash nodded. "To all of us. When he gets mad, I make him get mad at me so he won't hurt Mom or my sisters, but sometimes I can't stop it."

Paul slowly mixed the hot chocolate into a second cup and set it next to Flash. "What else has he done to you?"

"He burns us with cigarettes."

"Can you show me burns?"

The boy put down the stick and knife and rolled up his left sleeve. Paul saw several burn scars.

"Thanks for showing me, Flash."

"Are you going to arrest my dad?"

I want to kill your dad, Flash. "I want to help *you*. What do you think I should do?"

"Well, he's not my real dad, but Mom says if he is arrested, we will starve because we won't have any money."

"I'm not going to tell you it will be easy, but we can get your family help so you won't starve; and we can get you a place to stay for a while. Can your mom work?"

"She told me she wants to, but Dad won't let her."

"If your mom is willing to work, I'm sure we can get things sorted out to keep you guys safe and get you a place to live."

The boy started drinking his hot chocolate fast.

"Flash, slow down. We have all the time in the world."

He started drinking more slowly. As he did, he looked around. "I like it here."

"Me too. This area is an old Army fort, but now it's a park. In the daytime you can hike trails or walk along the beach almost forever. There's a big ol' bunker over that way and places where big cannons called mortars were. There's also small bunkers where there used to be machine guns. It's also a great place to share a campfire with a good friend."

"Am I your friend?"

"You certainly are, Flash."

The boy smiled that shy smile that Paul felt working its way into his heart. Flash finished his drink. He picked up the knife and held it out to Paul.

"Why don't you keep that?"

The boy's eyes grew large. "Really? For real?"

"Really for real. It's a Christmas present from me."

Flash held the knife in his hand and looked at it from every angle possible. "I've never had a Christmas present before."

"Well, it's about time you started getting some."

Flash looked up at Paul, tears falling down his cheeks. "Thank you, Paul."

After they finished their hot chocolate, Paul showed Flash how to put out a campfire and they walked back to the patrol car.

"Do I have to sit in the back."

Paul opened the front passenger door. "My friends always sit in the front."

When Paul got into the car, he saw Flash looking over the computer and radio equipment with great interest. Paul turned the car around.

"Think we ought to drive with our emergency lights on?"

"Can we, really?"

"Push that lever over to the right."

Red and blue light danced around the trees, to Flash's delight.

They drove to the intersection, and Paul told Flash to turn off the lights. It appeared that everybody was waiting at the park gate. Paul pulled up and stopped.

"You stay close to me, Flash."

"Okay, Paul." The fear was back in the boy's voice.

Paul got out and walked to the front of the car. He heard Flash close the door. He also heard a man say, "You little son-of-a-bitch." Suddenly a man bolted towards the boy's side of the car. Paul made three quick strides, caught the man by the throat, and kicked his legs out from under him, slamming him to the ground.

"You're under arrest," he growled.

Sgt. Long and Deputy Early ran up and helped him handcuff the man. Paul jerked him to his feet.

"You're under arrest for child abuse, aggravated assault, and torture."

"Y...you can't do this! You can't hit me like that."

Deputy Early took the man's arm. "I got him, Paul. It's my case."

"He can't hit me like that."

"Shut up," Early ordered.

The man started crying.

His wife walked up to him with tentative steps. "I can't believe it. You're just a bully. All this time, we put up with you knocking us around, and all you are is a coward."

The man started sobbing.

Paul let go of him and nodded to Early. He walked over to Flash. The boy plastered himself against Paul and hugged him tight.

Back at the Sheriff's Office in Coupeville, Paul was just finishing his paperwork when Sgt. Long and Katie Pearling from Child Protective Services came in to see him.

"We need to talk to you, Paul."

"What's up?"

"The mother in this case has warrants for her arrest for drug charges out of Oregon. She told Katie something you need to know about."

Katie sat down. "She told me she is a lousy mother and she never should've had kids."

"Great time to come to that conclusion," Paul said.

"Flash told his mother that he wants to live with you. Then, out of the blue, she told me she would be willing to relinquish her parental rights of her kids to you—but only if you took them all."

Paul sat speechless as a torrent of confusion and emotions ran through him. He finally stood up and started pacing. "Damn, I don't know. Julie and I want more kids, but not three all at once. I don't know if we can afford it. The house is big enough, but...."

Sgt. Long put his hands on Paul's shoulder. "You're babbling, Paul. This isn't something you have to do. It isn't even anything you have to decide tonight."

"There's just one big problem."

"What's that?"

"That damn Flash has wormed his way into my heart. I gotta call Julie."

It was Christmas Day. Paul sat at his kitchen table going over the family budget—again, and again. Flash and his sisters were asleep in the house. Paul's children, Tom and Emily, where in for a different Christmas surprise this morning. CPS and the Prosecutor's Office obtained a telephonic temporary custody order from a superior court judge, giving the custody to Paul and Julie.

There was a gentle knock at the front door. Paul looked at his watch. It was five in the morning. *Who in the world could that be?* He opened the door, and the Sheriff and Lt. Baker stood there with arm loads of Christmas gifts.

"Merry Christmas, Paul," the Sheriff said with a big grin.

"Sheriff, what's this all about?"

"It's all about the wonderful thing you and Julie are doing. I'm here to promise you the Sheriff's Office is one thousand percent behind you. We are going to do everything we can to help you out."

"Oh, I appreciate that, Sheriff, but I've been figuring things out. We'll be fine."

"So, you're telling me you have gifts for the new kids?"

"Well, no. Not enough time."

"Well, here you go then. These gifts are on time."

"Yes, sir. Thank you very much."

"Paul, you can't be shy about accepting help. I'm sure you and Julie will get things worked out, but you need some help right now. Deputies and officers from other jurisdictions on the island are passing the word, and you will be getting other things that you'll need. If you get too much, we'll pass it forward to another family."

"Thank you, Sheriff."

The men shook hands and the Sheriff and the Lieutenant left.

Paul went back to the table. He saw Flash walk into the living room. "What's up, Flash?"

Flash walked over to Paul, put his head against Paul's chest, and started crying. "I'm worried about my mom."

"That's perfectly understandable, buddy. We all worry about our moms."

"Will I ever see her again?"

"Before we left the Sheriff's Office, I gave your mom our address and phone number. I told her she could call and come visit anytime. It's up to her to decide to do those things."

Flash hugged Paul. "Thanks."

Paul put his hands on Flash's shoulders and looked into his eyes. "Flash, if anything is bothering you, you need to let me or Julie know. We can't help if we don't know."

Flash nodded his head and hugged Paul again.

"There you two are," Julie said as she led the other four children into the living room. "Everyone is anxious to see what Santa put under..." Julie's eyes grew wide as she looked under the tree. "Oh, my, I guess Santa worked overtime."

Paul gave Julie a wink. "Santa's helpers came by."

The word spread quickly among churches, civic clubs, and town merchants. So, not only were there three new children, but a flood of neighbors and members of the community came bearing Christmas gifts, envelopes stuffed with money, food, and news that several different charity drives were being planned on behalf of the family. Paul and Julie, completely bewildered, went through the motions of trying to deal with it all.

Later that evening, after everyone had left, Paul and Julie sat on their couch watching the children go over their Christmas gifts for the millionth time. Their son, who was two years younger than Flash, was already looking up to him as the big brother. Their daughter was about the same age as Flash's sisters, and they seemed to be getting along just fine. Julie put her head on Paul's shoulder.

"You notice how Flash has taken to the role of big brother?"

"The kid has already been through a tough, big brother boot camp." Paul took a deep breath. "You know we're in for good times and some hard times. You ready for all this? It isn't permanent yet."

"Are we a good team?"

"Yes, we are."

"Then, we'll make it work."

The ebb and flow of time washed over Whidbey Island as it does the world, bringing change over the years. But the island has a certain resistance to the kind of change that does more harm than good and seems to stubbornly maintain its character. Some say it's because of the island itself, with its mystical beauty. Others say it's also the character of the people who choose to call the island home.

"Did you call the Coupeville Marshal's Office, ma'am?"

"Yes, I did. There's a little boy curled up on the bench by the entrance to the wharf. It just isn't right at this time of night. I tried to talk to him, but he just kept on crying."

"Appreciate you calling, ma'am. I'll check it out."

The deputy marshal walked down to the entrance to the wharf from the caller's nearby condo and saw the boy on the bench. He noticed the moonlight shimmering on Penn Cove, outlining the wharf, a sight that always pleased him. He walked slowly so he wouldn't startle the kid and sat down next to him. The boy quickly sat up.

"Easy there, friend. No one is going to hurt you," the deputy assured him.

"Are you going to arrest me?"

"Are you a bad guy?"

"No, no, sir."

"Well, then I'm not going to arrest you." The early autumn night air was just getting a chilly bite to it. The deputy took off his jacket and put it around the boy. "What's your name?"

"Jake. What's your name?"

"My friends call me Flash," the deputy answered.

"Flash! Are you the real Flash?"

"I'm the real Flash on Whidbey Island."

"Am I really your friend?"

"Yes, you certainly are, Jake."

Other Books
By
Whidbey Writers' Group Authors

Barb Bland
Running Free

Pat Brunjes
Poetry from the Desert Floor
The Last Confession
The Girls Next Door

Miko Johnson
A Petal in the Wind I
A Petal in the Wind II – Lala Hafsetin
A Petal in the Wind III – The Great War
A Petal in the Wind IV – Lala Smetana

Gordon M. LaBuhn
Murder Has Two Faces
Murder Has Three Faces
My Gang

Mike McNeff
GOTU
Necessary Retribution
Hard Justice
Blood Wealth

Dorothy Read
End the Silence

Avis Rector
Carl Helps on the Farm
Pauline, A New Beginning on Whidbey Island

Bill Wilson
Stowaway
Offspring

Jan Wright
Dear Mrs. Wright, A Teacher's Memoir
Inspired by Students' Letters